Springhill Hospice

The Inspiring Story of
the People's Hospice
1983-1989
1989-2009

by
Diane Bailey-Ginever
Hospice Trustee

Published by Springhill Hospice
Rochdale

First published in paperback by Springhill Hospice, Rochdale
in 2009

A CIP record of this book is available from the British Library

ISBN 978-0-9563762-0-6

Typeset and printed by Saints Printers Ltd. Liverpool

Contents

This book is dedicated to:

My beloved husband Doug Ginever who died of non Hodgkin's Lymphoma in December 1994 but who never, unfortunately, benefitted from Springhill Hospice's love and care.

The thousands of patients and families who have received the very special care provided by Springhill Hospice in the years 1989 – 2009.

The many staff, volunteers and supporters of Springhill Hospice who, together, make its work, care and service possible.

The successful future of the Hospice and the care of its patients to come.

Preface

This book tells the story and pays tribute to so many people of Rochdale whose concerted efforts built Springhill Hospice. It was a labour of love and true commitment to a project that was dear to many who understood the principles of Hospice care.

The story covers our first twenty-five years from the birth of the Hospice Appeal to our 20th anniversary. The thousands of comments we have received proves it to be one of the most successful achievements by the people of Rochdale. They can wear its success with great pride and always strive to keep the doors open to all our patients and families who need our superb specialist care.

I pray the torch will continue to be borne by many generations to come as a jewel in Rochdale's crown.

Margaret J Geoghegan

"To see all these wonderful people caring and all the volunteers helping for free is an eye opener. The Hospice has done me the world of good"

A patient's comment from the booklet 'A world of good'
compiled by Hospice Trustee, Norman Frisby DL in 1999

"This is not a house of death; it is a place where life can be celebrated right to its end"

Margaret Geoghegan, MBE, Hospice Chairman 1987

"Palliative care is the active total care of patients whose disease is not responsive to curative treatment. Control of pain, of other symptoms and of psychological, social and spiritual problems is paramount"

The World Health Organization 1990

Foreword

I have visited Springhill Hospice on many occasions and found so much love and caring within its walls. Whether you have benefited from the calm restful loving care (and wonderful food), worked as a volunteer, been a member of staff or helped with fundraising, you have all made a contribution to the dream of Margaret Geoghegan who recognised the need for a haven of rest for the Rochdale Community. My heartfelt congratulations on your 20th Anniversary and may you continue to flourish.

Mary E Peters DBE LL

Acknowledgements

No author of a book like this can 'go it alone'. I have received amazing co-operation from everyone concerned with Rochdale's Springhill Hospice. People have shared their experiences, their stories and their enthusiasm with me. Archives were made available to me, as were personal scrapbooks and clipping collections.

I thank everyone who contributed to the wealth of information which I used. The good things in the book are theirs, any errors are mine.

It has not been possible to mention everyone who has contributed to the development of Springhill Hospice or who helped me in my research although some names feature. My apologies to anyone who has not been mentioned individually. The staff of Springhill Hospice have been indefatigable in tracking down facts and figures for me and most helpful in talking to me in great detail about their roles.

My thanks go in particular to those members of patients' families who spoke so movingly to me of the time their loved ones spent at Springhill and the wonderful care they received while there. My thanks also go to the indomitable Day Hospice patients who shared their thoughts with me.

Our thanks are due to the Rochdale Round Table for their generous contribution towards the cost of printing and publishing this book.

I also want to thank my friend and colleague Janice Power for interpreting my scrawl and typing several drafts of this book for me.

I appreciate enormously the efforts of my friends Kate Barker, Jane Graham and Alison Thaw in reading various drafts and offering useful and encouraging comments.

Photograph of author courtesy of Trevor Adams, Accrington.

Introduction

In October 2009 Springhill Hospice Rochdale will have been open and caring for patients for 20 years.

In that time over 6,000 people from Rochdale and the surrounding areas have benefited from the services and hospitality of the Hospice.

The dates on the cover of this book represent a period of 26 years rather than just the 20 years of operation. This reflects the fact that the inspiring story of Springhill Hospice began with the launch of the Hospice Appeal six years before it opened to look after patients in 1989. The amazing determination, vision, mutual help and public support of the period 1983 – 1989 need to be recognized in addition to telling the story of the first 20 years of operation and service. The Hospice began with an idea, devotion and determination. The pages which follow describe the journey from 1983 to 2009. They also describe the Hospice as it is now.

This book is written in nine separate sections. You can choose how to read it. You can start at Section 1 and read sequentially through to Section 9. Or, you can start with any section which interests you and read through the other sections in any order which pleases you. Section 9 is not a narrative, it is a year by year timeline 1983 – 2009. Not everything in the timeline is mentioned in the book. It is impossible to cover everything which happened over 25 years but I have included the information for the sake of making a complete record.

I hope you enjoy reading this book as much as I enjoyed researching and writing it. It truly is an inspiring story and the Hospice is a wonderful place which constantly seeks to improve and develop while offering an exemplary standard of care to patients with life threatening or life limiting diseases.

1. HOW WE STARTED

On the cold afternoon of Spring Day, March 21st 1987, over 400 men, women and children, most armed with spades, trooped excitedly up the hill of Broad Lane. This happy sight was the culmination of years of fund-raising, organization, planning and dedication. The date was chosen because of the link between 'Spring Day' and 'Spring Hill'.

The spade carriers had responded to an advertisement placed in the Rochdale Observer by the Hospice Appeal Trustees. The advert asked supporters of the Hospice for Rochdale Appeal to come and help cut the first sods before work truly began on the building which was to be Springhill Hospice. As the Hospice had no spades itself the advertisement invited those attending to bring their own. They did, even tiny children helped with their toy spades.

It snowed in the morning of March 21st 1987 but at lunchtime the sun came out. Then Margaret Geoghegan (later to be awarded an MBE) cut the first sod, helped by the gang of 400. Balderstone School, at the start of the association which lasts to the present time, helped with the sod cutting ceremony. The school loaned us their building on Queen Victoria Street for the day and a group of students treated the event as a project. They brought food for the participants, prepared a buffet and served it to the enthusiastic sod cutters and others who attended this long awaited event. The pupils later sold the food left over to those present and contributed the money raised to the Hospice Appeal. A local florist provided, free of charge, a lovely table decoration and pots of polyanthus. The latter were given as souvenirs to guests at the event.

The dream and vision which had inspired so many people and engendered so much support and affection since 1983 was about to become reality and Rochdale was on the way to having its own Hospice.

It all began in early 1983. At that point, Margaret Geoghegan had spent many years as a busy volunteer contributing much to the Rochdale community. She had years of experience on the Rochdale Community Health Council; as a member of Rochdale Health Authority; as member of Age Concern and as a Member of the Social Services Appeals Tribunal. In the early1980s she was working as a Ward Clerk on a male medical ward at Birch Hill and saw many patients suffering from lung cancer. This, coupled with the deaths of her parents in hospital and her husband Michael at home from cancer led her to identify the very real need in Rochdale for palliative care in the specialist surroundings of a Hospice.

Mrs Geoghegan talked a lot about Rochdale needing its own Hospice rather than having to rely on others, geographically distant from the Borough. Her work at

Birch Hill as a ward clerk meant that she was involved in trying to find places for gravely ill people in other Hospices throughout the North West. It was heart breakingly difficult and she saw often, at first hand, the difficulties experienced by families struggling to manage at home with terminally ill relatives. At the time many people needed this further, different care but provision was very limited as the only Hospices which then existed nearby were in Yorkshire or Cheshire. The seed of an idea was planted and gradually grew to the point that the initiative developed its own momentum and swept people along with it. Rochdale was to have its own Hospice.

"We need a Hospice in Rochdale" Margaret Geoghegan told anyone who would listen. When asked by colleagues what she intended to do on her retirement she replied *"I'm going to start an appeal for a Hospice for Rochdale"*.

She went out fact finding, talking to doctors and nurses, to people at other Hospices and at The Christie Hospital in Manchester. She wanted to learn from the mistakes and successes of others and to ensure that the Rochdale Hospice offered cutting edge facilities.

The story of how that idea became reality after a period of six years is both inspiring and fascinating. It is a story of devotion and determination and is an indication of what people can achieve when they share a vision and work together towards it.

The Appeal for a Hospice for Rochdale was kicked off by a £5.00 donation from a colleague of Mrs Geoghegan. Incidentally, this colleague, Mrs June Law, attended the May 2008 opening and dedication ceremony of the major extension of Springhill. After the initial start, Mrs Geoghegan collected together a group of like-minded Rochdalians: doctors, a banker, nurses, a solicitor, friends and sympathisers. They had their first meeting at a friend's house, that of Mrs Betty Portman, in January 1983. The laborious formalities for creating a trust that would satisfy the powers-that-be of the Charity Commissioners were set in motion.

A constitution was drafted by Mr Steven Price, who is still a Trustee of Springhill. The constitution stated that the purpose of the Appeal was: *"To establish, maintain and manage a Hospice or hospital for the relief of pain and suffering among the terminally ill and for the treatment of disease, pain and suffering"*. The constitution was adopted on April 15th 1983 and paved the way for further action.

Rochdale Parish Church Hall, St Chad's Fold, was booked for a public meeting on the evening of May 8th 1983 to launch the appeal, with other meetings scheduled at Middleton and Heywood.

Would anyone turn up? The organisers were nervous but the Fold caretaker greeted them with *"I've put all 200 chairs out. It's going to be a great evening"*. It was, the initial worry was needless. The hall was packed with interested and excited people.

And it was an exhilarating evening. The Mayor and Mayoress, Councillor and Mrs Robert Stott came, as did representatives of the Health Authority and it was standing room only with folk from all walks of life in Rochdale. Margaret Geoghegan made a speech and answered questions and as people went home they dropped pound notes and fivers on to a table near the door. When planning the meeting, no one had thought about holding a collection!

That was the start of a Hospice for Rochdale. The first sod was cut almost exactly four years later, after a mammoth fund-raising effort.

An appeal letter was drafted and went out to the community of Rochdale in mid 1983. The letter asked for the vast sum of £250,000 *"to enable us to fund a Hospice in the Rochdale area"*.

"This," it explained, *"will provide a caring service, more personal and specialised than can be provided in hospitals"*. The letter went on to say:

"A Hospice is a haven and refuge with hospitality for patients and their families..........."

"The support of families is very important to us, not only while their loved ones are under our care in the Hospice or at home, but also when our nursing is no longer required..............."

"The emphasis in a Hospice is on care, compassion and pain-relief........."

"Pain can be controlled in many ways using the most up-to-date techniques, and this enables the patient to live an almost pain-free life, taking part in day-to-day living and enjoying a greater quality of life....."

"The Hospice would be open to all, the only qualification being NEED, and it would be free"

The letter ended with the heartfelt plea:

"PLEASE HELP US TO ACHIEVE OUR AIM BY RESPONDING TO OUR APPEAL FUND".

The people of Rochdale responded magnificently and have continued to do so, right up to the present. After 26 years Springhill continues to prove the truth of the words of the founder of the Hospice movement in the UK, Dame Cicely Saunders. Dame Cicely said *"You matter because you are you and you matter to the end of your life. We will do all we can not only to help you die peacefully but also to live until you die"*. Springhill does this faithfully.

On June 4th 1983 it was announced that £1,744 had been raised in the first month of the appeal. It was a start. The snowball had started rolling. From the outset the founders of the appeal were determined that all would be business-like and transparent.

Mr Roy Pickup who worked with Rochdale Council was loaned to the Hospice Appeal. He was to oversee the business aspects of the set-up. Later Mrs Dorothy Ashton took over this aspect of the Appeal and worked closely with the Trustees.

Now that money was coming in it had to be managed well and transparently. John Dafforne, who is still a Trustee of the Hospice, came on board at a meeting in March 1983. He took on the responsibility of managing the money which came in from many sources. All cash received went to John and was receipted every Sunday. John got the Rochdale Observer involved and it used to print monthly lists of donations in order to thank those who contributed and to encourage other people to give. This activity on the part of the Observer was the start of a 25 year collaboration with and active support of the Hospice. Contributions came from darts teams, local football teams, many small organizations and individuals. All gave money, many regularly. From the start Rochdale took the Hospice to its heart. The original estimate of the funds needed was £800,000, a huge sum. This sum could easily have daunted the Committee and the people of Rochdale but it didn't, it focused minds and energies. In the event the original estimate of £800,000 had to be increased to £900,000 to pay for the building but Rochdale made it.

The people of Rochdale responded amazingly to the enormous demand. Supermarket collections, three-legged pub-crawls, coffee mornings, toy sales, sponsored parachute jumps, bike rides and fun runs were among the many tactics used. Cub packs and pensioners, slimming clubs and carol singers all responded. And day after day, the legendary 'Anon' made his or her mystery gift. By December 1983 the total raised had reached £27,581. This is how the money came in: *"From Ros's mum £3, sponsored bike ride up Snowdon £1,602.00, carol singers £75.23, tea cup reading £35, Rounders' League £533, "We didn't send Christmas cards" £15.00"*. On and on went the avalanche of contributions.

Now that money was coming in and the support of Rochdale had been achieved the work really began. A Committee was established, this comprised Margaret Geoghegan as Chairman, Michael Schofield as Secretary, John Dafforne as

Treasurer, Steven Price as Legal Adviser, Drs. David Foster (physician) and Diane Humphrey (anaesthetist) as Medical Advisers and Viv Williamson, District Nurse. Betty Portman was also a member of this original committee. She helped to open and manage the first retail outlets once the Hospice was established. Later Robert Clegg (now Councillor Clegg) joined the Committee as Secretary.

A 20-bed unit was projected, *"which"*, said the Rochdale Committee, *"will allow people to live and die with dignity, in a loving and caring peaceful atmosphere where, instead of counting days, each day will be made to count"*. Mrs Geoghegan said *"This is not a house of death but one of life and dignity"*. So today it remains, Springhill really is a place of life, of dignity, of humour and affection. When I spoke to her, Dame Mary Peters, a Patron of Springhill, commented on the atmosphere of love which permeates the Hospice. This comment about a pervading atmosphere of love was made to me by many people including the families of patients.

Now that the Hospice Appeal was launched and money was coming in, the search for a site to develop began. Rochdale Council planners came up with 27 possible sites across the town. Some were hopeless, some were possible. The Committee spent weekend after weekend looking at open fields and mud. One site was ideal and it was chosen. This was land off Broad Lane, Buersil, the site of an old house called Spring Hill.

While sites were being explored, other visits were made to existing and newly built Hospices to talk to their staff and patients and to see what was needed. It made sense to learn from other's mistakes and successes and not to have to reinvent the wheel.

In January 1985 the Springhill Appeal Committee invited their colleagues from St Ann's Hospice, Heald Green, Cheadle to view the Broad Lane Spring Hill site. At that time it was completely open land with few buildings. The open vista, ringed by snow-topped hills, was stunning and so beautiful. In fact, the site is still beautiful although somewhat more built up. The Hospice gardens and surrounding fields, often containing horses, can be seen from most patients' rooms and other parts of the Hospice and bring great pleasure to patients, their families, other visitors and Hospice staff. Squirrels and birds attracted to the food placed outside regularly add to the delight of those in the Hospice building as do the changing seasons of trees, plants and flowers, all lovingly tended by the Hospice gardener and his volunteers.

In the early days of the Rochdale Appeal, Bury was also planning a Hospice. There were early discussions about building a combined Hospice for both areas but in 1984 a public vote was held and it was decided that Rochdale would go it alone and how it did so! The design of the Hospice started in November 1984 with an original estimated cost of £1,140,850. This sum was well above the Committee's budget and was revised downwards to £800,000. By June 1984 we had £65,000 in the bank and were well on our way. Also in 1984 the plan and appeal received a boost in that the Mayor, Councillor Norman Angus, made the Hospice Appeal his charity for his year of office 1984/85.

In the early stages of the appeal, Margaret Geoghegan spoke to over 200 groups of people to raise awareness of the appeal and attended many conferences talking about the Hospice and developments. Her enthusiasm and commitment were contagious and people of all sorts became interested.

The design team was getting down to the details. There would, it was decreed, be paper on the walls, carpet on the floors. There was not to be even a whiff of the 'institutional'. It might be difficult to disguise a medical bed, but there would be counterpanes down to the floor. Nothing would be too good for the patients of Rochdale's Hospice. The Hospice was to be a comfortable home, as far as possible, not a hospital. Building began a week after the first sods were cut on 21st March 1987.

The Council lawyers drew up a lease. It ran to 15 jargon-packed pages. The Council, it said, *"demised"* to the Hospice Trustees *"three point nought acres or thereabouts situated at Springhill, Broad Lane"*. The Council reserved their rights to *"all mines and minerals, sand and gravel, under or upon the land"*. The land could only, they insisted, be used for a Hospice and the Trustees could not allow it to be used *"for illegal or immoral purpose"*. The financial terms were, thankfully, generous. The Council would donate the land without cost. This truly was a magnificent gesture and was hugely appreciated. The Council has since generously donated further land as the Hospice has extended.

The land on which the Hospice is built and which contains its grounds is on a long leasehold agreement and is leased by the Rochdale Metropolitan Borough Council(MBC) to the Hospice in consideration of a premium of £26,000 for a term of 99 years. This sum was donated by Rochdale MBC and the Trustees covenanted to repay the sum in the event that the land ever ceased to be used for charitable purposes. This enormous generosity was a huge benefit for the Hospice and gave us a marvellous start.

The 24th of April 1985 was a red letter day. The Borough of Rochdale handed over the lease of the Broad Lane site to the Trustees. As I've already said; the land was given at no cost by the Council and Margaret Geoghegan dubbed this *"a piece of generosity which crossed all boundaries of politics and religion"*. She felt that it symbolised the community coming together to work for something which it needed. This was reported in the Rochdale Observer. At that point we had raised

£272,984. One week after the sod cutting ceremony, 21st March 1987, work began on the site. Going ahead with building before the whole sum was raised was an act of faith and that faith was fulfilled as funds continued to come in.

In an attempt to gain support from the 'authorities', Mrs Geoghegan wrote, on behalf of the Appeal, to Sir John Page, Chair of the Regional Health Authority asking for help. There was, at the time, no formal policy to deal with such a request but Sir John offered practical support in the form of a design team of three people which included an architect, Mr A Potts, an engineer, Mr J Sunderland and a quantity surveyor, Mr J Kemp. This generosity saved the Appeal many thousands of pounds and provided a really professional basis for the design and building of Springhill. Mr Potts and Mr Sunderland were both Trustees of the Hospice for a long time before retiring.

On 31st October 1987 the foundation stone was laid by Members of Parliament Sir Cyril Smith and Mr Geoffrey Dickens on behalf of the people of Rochdale. Some dignitaries present expressed some mild disquiet about the ambitious venture and its attendant risks. Mrs Geoghegan responded briskly by saying they would be invited the following year to the topping out of the roof – and they were. The building was topped out in 1988 by Mr Ronald Taylor, Mayor of Rochdale.

The builders were GS Seddon who had accidentally seen some Hospice plans and expressed an interest. In fact they built Springhill for *"cost plus £1"*. This generosity was an amazing fillip for the Hospice. Seddons also offered the Trustees huge moral support by, for example, suggesting that the building be started before all the necessary funding was in place, as it would encourage people to continue, or begin, giving. The sight of the physical start of the building certainly seemed to encourage people to give. *"If you don't start now your costs will go up considerably"* the builders told the Committee. Mr J Sunderland, the engineer, who was later both Trustee and Vice President of the Hospice worked closely with Seddons and oversaw all plans and developments.

When the design for the Hospice was agreed, it was such that the building could be developed bit by bit so that when certain stages were reached work could be halted if necessary and the building sealed off until the next tranche of funding became available. In the event this facility was never required. Funding kept pace with development although there were a few, temporary 'hairy' moments.

By the 17th February 1988 the building was watertight and, up to then, had cost £225,000 to build. This was make or break week, a decision had to be made by the Board whether to take up the contractor's offer to mothball the building until all the money had been raised, or to continue with the building. Finance in the bank was £381,947 including a £45,000 legacy which had just come in. The Trustees decided to continue with the building and to seek some satisfactory borrowing arrangement from the bank should this be considered necessary (fortunately it wasn't). Over five years a total of £600,000 had been raised towards the newly revised target of £900,000. This was a magnificent response from Rochdale and its people. It was, at the time, the biggest ever fund-raising effort in Rochdale and was seen as clear testimony of the degree of support Rochdale offered its own Hospice.

The unbelievable kindness of the people and businesses of Rochdale continued as the building rose. For example, Seddons, the builders, paid for a watchman to guard the site after vandals had burnt down the hut which contained the original plans for the building. The building continued with Trustee meetings taking place on site as the walls grew.

In October 1988, before the building was even finished, Mrs Kay Scott, a Nursing Manager from Birch Hill was recruited and appointed as the first Matron of Springhill Hospice. She was, in fact, the first ever employee of the Hospice. She worked alone, other than having contact with Trustees and builders, as the building was completed and until February 1989 when Dr Robert (Bob) Gartside joined the Hospice as part time Hospice Doctor.

During this initial period of her employment, Mrs Scott faced and dealt with the task of equipping the Hospice with all necessary furniture, equipment and supplies. The planners of the Hospice developed a shopping list to assist Mrs Scott in outfitting the building. *"Can you help us?"* they asked the people of Rochdale. *"Here is what we need:*

- *Beds and bedding, of course, for wards – 22 beds at £418.00 each*
- *Pots and pans for the kitchens – and £400 worth of cutlery*
- *Desks £130.23 for nurses and typists*
- *A medical library: £2,000.*

And also

- *four stepladders, £30 each*
- *28 wastepaper bins at £1.95p*
- *141 name badges for volunteers at 43p*
- *12 filing trays at £4.20*
- *six clocks, £14.00 each, and much, much more."*

The money came in and the necessary items were bought one by one. On one occasion some special wheeled chairs costing £3,000 were ordered, in hope because there was no cash available. What happened? – a letter arrived out of the blue containing a donation of £3,000! So often in the early days our guardian angel helped through the generosity of businesses, individuals and groups. The angel is still hard at work!

In addition to equipping the building, Mrs Scott also managed the task of bringing the first staff, clinical and administrative teams on board. In speaking of the team she was putting together for Springhill, she said *"The Hospice staff will go out of their way to help patients and their families to come to terms with the situation. We can give a lot of support and improve the quality of life of patients".*

Before joining the Hospice, Mrs Scott was a Nursing Officer at Birch Hill Hospital. At the age of 18 she had seen her own mother die in a lot of pain at Birch Hill. This had been the start of a heartfelt desire on her part to do more for the terminally ill. At her appointment Mrs Scott said *"I have known some nurses who have never been taught how to cope with death. Death will never be easy, but we can do a lot to help".*

This belief underlined everything the newly appointed Matron did at Springhill Hospice during her seven years in charge (she retired in 1996). She set a high standard of clinical care and of mutual support between Hospice staff. Her work and dedication enabled the trustees to establish the foundation for the continuing success of the Hospice of Rochdale. We all owe her a big debt of gratitude.

The building grew, slowly at first but then more rapidly. The first meeting of the Trustees actually to take place in the Hospice building was on March 14th 1989. Prior to this, meetings had taken place at Birch Hill Hospital, Rochdale Infirmary or the home of Mrs Portman.

One amusing story from these early days concerns the elderly Trustee who suddenly went missing from a meeting with no explanation. As the site was a mess and contained a huge hole, panic mounted as the missing Trustee could not be found. It was feared that an accident had happened. Another Trustee, always impeccably dressed, was about to climb down into the hole to find out if there had been an unfortunate event when it transpired that the 'missing' person had simply taken the offer of a lift home and gone off without telling anyone. Huge relief and giggles all round. This story, when I heard it, was the catalyst which made me decide to capture some of the early history of the Hospice by writing this book. There are so many amusing and amazing stories surrounding those early days. Amusing things still happen and the Hospice is a place of much fun and laughter as well as being one which offers exemplary levels of care and support to patients and families.

The building was finally completed and handed over to the Hospice Committee in December1988, the cost of the building being £850,336.33. The running costs of Springhill were estimated, at the time, at £500,000 per year. We supported ourselves from the outset with the never-ending generosity of the people of Rochdale. If I mention this generosity often it is because it never ceases to amaze and inspire awe in everyone connected with the running of Springhill.

On the 7th of November 1988 The company called Springhill Hospice (Rochdale) Ltd was formed. It was incorporated on the 7th of December of the same year. The first directors were:

Mrs M. Geoghegan	Chairman
Mr J. Dafforne	(resigned 3.3.92 to take up post as paid Company Secretary, on retiring from this role he rejoined the Board as a Trustee))
Mrs B. Portman	
Mrs V. Williamson	
Dr D. Humphrey	(resigned 5.1.93, moved from area)
Mr M. Schofield	(resigned 3.12.91)
Mr J. Sunderland	
Mr R. Clegg	
Mr R. Pickup	(was appointed paid Company Secretary)
Mr A. Potts	
Dr D. Foster	
Mr S. Price	
Mr J Sweetmore	

The Hospice took in its first two in-patients in October 1989. There were 25 staff in place by this point and the two patients were from Middleton.

The building was officially opened on 2nd November, 1989 by HRH the Princess Royal. She was so intrigued by the place and the people she met that she caused her entourage quite some concern because she stayed and stayed, ignoring her demanding schedule. The Hospice had pulled all the stops out for the Royal visit. We even borrowed a solid sliver tray and tea service from the Town Hall in an effort to create a good impression. It wasn't needed as the patients, the staff and the buildings of Springhill were in themselves all that was needed to impress. One amusing thing which happened during HRH's visit was the double take which resulted when she met Dr Diana Humphrey who looked very like her.

After its fascinating beginning and the first 20 years of operation the Hospice is now a £2.7m business with the equivalent of 63 full time staff (equivalent to 88 people in total), 250 volunteers at the main building and a further 109 at the shops and an unshakeable commitment to the service of the people of Rochdale and its surroundings areas.

The symbol of Springhill Hospice shows a candle protected by a roof. The almost burned-out candle represents a life coming to a close. The still burning flame is the still bright spirit which is sheltered by the roof of the Hospice which provides comfort and support for both patient and family.

And the colour green?

That was decided upon by the early fund-raisers after a frantic search through colour charts, pattern books, much studying of swatches of curtain and furnishing materials. At last the ideal shade was spotted….. in the colour of a chain-store carrier bag.

Green is a peaceful relaxing colour, and often used where calm and quiet is needed. Think of the green room in a theatre where the cast relaxes between acts.

Other sections of this book provide information on patients, the staff, the services of Springhill Hospice and such issues as fund-raising and the building itself.

2. WHAT'S IT ALL ABOUT?
What is a Hospice?

The word 'Hospice' has existed in the English language and others, for a long time. High on the fells above Cartmel, in the Lake District, is an old grey stone building known as a Hospice where Monks from the nearby Priory looked after travellers and the ill during the Middle Ages. On the waterfront in Genoa, Northern Italy is a huge stone building where the Knights Templar looked after their ill and wounded colleagues and the poor and ill of the town at the time of the Crusades. Medieval Hospices provided food and shelter for travellers on Europe's defined Pilgrim routes. They also cared for the sick and dying.

There are many, many such early Hospices across Europe. The early Hospices were imbued with some of the philosophy of today's Hospices in that they were all about caring for people. But their care ranged further than today's Hospices do in that they seem to have acted as a cross between local hospitals and social support networks. Today's Hospices specialize in delivering care to people affected by terminal illnesses, mostly those with cancer but also those with other life-limiting diseases, and their families, both via in-patient bedded units, day care coverage and, where possible, in their own homes. 'Hospice' is not a building, it is a philosophy. It is an attempt to develop a way of caring which offers an improved quality of living, when a full cure is no longer expected or possible. It works to ensure that life is lived to the full to the very end and that patients' last days are as good as they possibly can be.

The Hospice philosophy places paramount importance on pain and symptom control and comfort, it unites medical and nursing skills and care for the whole person's needs, respects each person's right to knowledge and freedom of choice – where possible, and gives a sense of reasonable confidence and security. It recognizes that dying and grieving are stressful but that they are part of life. It also recognizes the pressures placed on close family and friends and offers sensitive, on-going support in a variety of ways.

Springhill's 16 bedded in-patient unit exists to offer specialist medical, nursing and support services to adult patients who are terminally ill or who have life limiting diseases and to their carers/family members, with a comprehensive programme of physical, emotional, spiritual and social support.

Springhill is part of a wider Hospice community. There are more than 240 Hospices in the UK alone and hundreds, if not thousands more world-wide. These Hospices care for adults and children living with life-limiting and terminal illnesses. Care is completely free to patients and families. A National Audit Office study found that in 2006 Hospices in the UK supported 38,000 people with in-patient facilities. A further 112,000 patients and family members were cared for in the community in the same year. These figures are amazing, particularly when one considers that most funding of Hospice care comes from local charity fund-raising. Only about one third of the costs are met by the Government from tax payers' money. In 2007, £313 million pounds was donated or bequeathed to the Hospice movement. This colossal sum represented an average of £5 for each person; child and adult, in the UK. The real growth of today's Hospice movement with its holistic or all embracing definition of care began with the work of Dame Cicely Saunders whose St Christopher's Hospice opened in 1967 in Sydenham, London.

Hospice care extends to families and friends of patients through services such as advice and support for people caring for loved ones at home and counselling and bereavement services. In 2009 Springhill was given a grant and appointed, for the first time, a Carers' Co-ordinator. This person worked to support carers of patients in a range of ways and to explore how best to help carers. The project helped us to understand carers' needs better and to plan to meet them more effectively.

Patient care is provided via a range of services which includes pain control, symptom relief, skilled nursing care, counselling, complementary therapies, physiotherapy, creative activities and spiritual/religious care. Hospitals deal with the patient and the illness and are designed to cure illnesses and ailments. Hospices care for all aspects of the whole person and their life and for their families and carers. Hospices are mainly about making the end of life as happy and comfortable as possible. In caring for patients Hospices often have to treat the underlying illness. This may sometimes be supported by treatment at a nearby hospital if relevant but, as appropriate, doctors at Springhill will continue to treat underlying illnesses. Sometimes, however, the patient's illness may be too far advanced for any appropriate active treatment to be helpful and palliative care is what is most appropriate.

One name which figures largely in the history and development of the Hospice movement in the UK is that of Dame Cicely Saunders. She qualified in medicine in her 30s, in the late 1950s. Just before she qualified she was working on her first publication in which she set out the basis of a new approach to the care of the terminally ill. This important first paper was published in 1958 in the St Thomas's Hospital Gazette. She was the first modern doctor to dedicate her entire career to the care of those at the end of their lives. She suggested in this keynote paper that many patients felt deserted by their doctor at the end of their lives. She believed that, in an ideal situation, the doctor should remain the centre of a team which, even when it could no longer heal, would work together to relieve pain and symptoms and to bring hope and consolation to the patient at the end.

By the end of the 1950s the British National Health Service had been in existence for over 10 years. It pledged to provide care from the cradle to the grave. However, the new service had put nothing in place to promote the care of the dying. Its policy was concerned with acute medicine and rehabilitation. At that time there was only a handful of homes for the dying across the world. Cicely Saunders was one of a few doctors who began to take an interest in the care of the dying. She embarked on a ten year programme of research, discussion and innovation which ended with the opening of St Christopher's Hospice in Sydenham, London in the late 1960s. This was the first in the line of Hospices in the UK. It is this philosophy and attitude to care which informs the work of all at Springhill Hospice. We carry on the marvellous tradition established by Dame Cicely Saunders in the mid 20th Century.

Today Springhill Hospice is at the forefront of Hospice work and care. It has won many awards for all aspects of its activities from clinical care to the standard of its food and grounds. For example, its shops are amongst the most profitable in the charity sector. (In 2008 – 2009 our profit was 56% of total takings. The national average profit is 20%). At present, in early 2009, Springhill has begun to explore actively the provision of Hospice at Home. This would take Hospice care into the homes of patients and further facilitate choice about where they are cared for and choice about where they die. It will be some time before our research results in recommendations. We will continue to consult with the people of Rochdale to determine what is needed and what is possible.

One problem faced by Springhill and other Hospices is the misconceptions held by some people. There is a misplaced fear of Hospices in that some people see them only as places where seriously ill people go to die. Many may feel that Hospices must be gloomy, miserable and depressing places. My own husband, when seriously ill with cancer would not countenance going to the Hospice because he strongly held this view. Nothing could be further from the truth. In no way is Springhill Hospice sad or gloomy. It is bright, welcoming and comfortable, in total contrast to the usual hospital atmosphere. It is still a major regret for me that Doug died in a sterile comfortless hospital room. No greater contrast with what happens at Springhill could be imagined. That awful night while at Doug's side from 9pm to 5am when he finally died, I sat in a hard comfortless chair. The only refreshment I had was a cup of coffee fetched from a machine for me by the friend who had driven me to the hospital. The staff were pleasant and business-like but strangely detached. The night a week earlier when Doug had been rushed into hospital by ambulance I was told I could stay with him overnight. I did, but not in a charming comfortable room such as those which Springhill makes available for patients' families but in his bleak room on a narrow hard chair-bed from which both the sheet and I kept slipping.

Misconceptions about Hospices being doom, gloom and misery are totally wrong.

Anyone who enters Springhill's reception area immediately begins to understand that this is a place of light, love and caring and, often, laughter. Further time spent in the Day Hospice, the ward and the gardens begins rapidly to dispel and change all negative perceptions. Dame Mary Peters, a patron of Springhill, says that of all her connections with charities, Springhill is particularly dear to her. She commented that love is all present in the building and the staff and that it is a place of positive hope and care. Right at the start Mrs Geoghegan said that *"This is not a house of death; it is a place where life can be celebrated right to its end"*. It is understandable that some people have negative perceptions, after all most of us are frightened of death and dying. People don't always want to hear the detail of the operational and clinical side of Springhill's work. Fear stops some people from listening to the very positive aspects of Hospice work. We put a lot of effort into dispelling negative perceptions of Hospice work. Our best advocates are patients and their families. We know that 99.9% of people who have experience of Springhill's work and service feel that it is wonderful place and that it does a wonderful job. You can read some of their views in Section 3. We welcome anyone who wants to find out more about the Hospice and are happy to arrange a tour of the premises for them. Many patients and their families come to visit and explore the facilities before agreeing to come in either as an in-patient or to Day Hospice sessions. Some patients arrive ill and fearful but soon relax into the comforting surroundings and begin to appreciate the huge difference between the Hospice and a hospital.

Over half of our in-patients each year are discharged back to their home and families with their symptoms under control and their pain lessened.

All Hospices differ in size and activity but share the same ethos. Some general organizations support them, for example, 'Help the Hospices' is the leading charity supporting Hospice care throughout the UK. Their website: www.helpthehospices.org.uk provides information useful to patients, carers, families or others who have an interest in Hospice and palliative care.

The National End of Life Care strategy published by the Department of Health in 2008 presents Help the Hospice and other caring institutions with an opportunity to embed Hospice values and principles throughout the whole care system in England. Hospices are key to helping people accept that dying is part of the experience of life and in providing choice for patients so that they can live well until they die, wherever that may be. Springhill Hospice works closely with Macmillan and Marie Curie nurses, residential homes and hospitals to assist with the further application and extension of Hospice values and care.

Despite the awe-inspiring generosity of people in general, Hospices, like other charities, may experience a shortfall in funding in the recession of 2009. It is quite important that many people do not realise that Hospices are charities and are therefore heavily dependent on charitable giving. Springhill expends a lot of time and effort in raising awareness of our work and activities. We have many, many long-term friends and supporters whom we value enormously but it is vitally important that we continue to make new friends and attract new supporters.

The current financial situation may adversely affect Springhill and other Hospices as money becomes tight. However, the picture across the UK varies and some Hospices will have few financial worries. David Prail, Chief Executive of Help the Hospices said that *"Hospices, by their nature, are used to change and challenge and therefore equipped to deal with these (difficult) times as they have done before. Hospices are innovative in the way they fund-raise and manage services as they have always had to be so. Service cut backs would only happen as a last resort as Hospices are seeking other ways to maximise income and restrict or cut costs"*. At Springhill efforts have begun and will continue to raise funds and restrict costs.

It is important to maintain and fund the work of Hospices not just because of the advantages for patients and their families but because the £484 million pounds collectively spent annually in the UK by the local independent charitable Hospices supplements the work of the NHS by £1.3 million per day and enables specific palliative care to be available where its is needed in home-like and comforting circumstances.

In 1999, in our 10th year Norman Frisby DL (Deputy Lieutenant), a Trustee and long time supporter of Springhill researched and wrote a publication called 'A World of Good' to commemorate the 10th Anniversary. The title came from the words of a patient who had first hand experience of the loving care provided by Springhill since it opened in 1989. She said: *"To see all these wonderful people caring and all the volunteers helping for free is an eye opener. The Hospice has done me the world of good"*. The booklet 'A World of Good' was published in 1999 in place of our Annual Report or the Springhillian.

Section 3 of this book provides further information on our patients.

3. OUR PATIENTS

As I have said elsewhere in this book, our patients are our only reason for being here and for our work during the last 20 years. In October 1989 our first two patients, both from Middleton, came to be treated at Springhill Hospice. With this event six years of intense activity, great hopes, faith and initial fund-raising came to an end. Rochdale had its Hospice and the first twenty years of caring began. Since October 1989, many patients and their families have received the special loving care which is the essence of Springhill. Over 6,000 patients from across the borough of Rochdale have been looked after. A majority of these left the Hospice with their symptoms under control and their quality of life improved. Today 55% of our in-patients return to their home

From the outset, most of the beds in Springhill's in-patient unit were reserved for cancer patients. Two beds were allocated to other life limiting diseases, mainly, at the start, neurological. Now these beds provide respite care for a range of illnesses, including MS, Motor Neurone, Aids and serious heart conditions.

Over the last 20 years, adult patients of all ages have come to Springhill, men and women, young and not so young. Each patient is a person whose life, and that of their family, had been adversely affected by disease. Many patients may have entered the Hospice reluctantly and maybe fearfully but after a day or two all feel safe and cared for. Worried family members see their loved ones well supported in all ways, clinically, spiritually and emotionally. The work of the Hospice with patients frees their families to be family members rather than carers and therefore can usually help family relationships. Springhill does a lot more than offer the highest quality of clinical care. It supplements pain and symptom control with complementary therapies, spiritual support and a willingness to be flexible and supportive in meeting individual needs. Springhill has in-patients and day care patients. In-patients on average spend 14 or 15 days at Springhill. Some are here for a day or two; others may occasionally stay for 10 or 12 weeks. Unlike some Hospices, Springhill does not have a policy which dictates a maximum length of patient stay. The patient's illness and needs will determine both the treatment given and the length of time they stay with us.

Our in-patients come to us through a variety of routes. GPs, hospitals or even family members can initiate contact with Springhill. The Admissions Co-ordinator will follow up on any referral or request for admission in order to establish the necessary information about the person who wants to come to Springhill. Once it has been agreed that someone can come in to stay with us, we do all we can to ensure that the admission happens as quickly as possible, generally it does not take more than a couple of days from referral to admission.

Once patients are admitted they are visited by one of the Hospice doctors and their care and treatment is identified. The clinical care provided at Springhill is second to none and is concentrated on pain and symptom control and the maximizing of patient comfort. A multidisciplinary team meets regularly to discuss the full range of patients needs; including social and spiritual aspects of care.

Patients' needs can vary day-to-day. The care provided for individuals is related to their level of dependency, which can vary from low to very high. The higher the level of dependency the more care the patient requires. Each group of patients will vary in terms of their illness and their levels of dependency. If most patients have high levels of dependency Sheila Johnson, Clinical Services Manager, and Sister Ann Gray, Senior Nursing Sister, respond by assessing the staff levels needed and, where necessary, use 'Bank' staff to support the permanent nursing team. These are our own nurses but are used less often as we keep a high level of trained staff on rota. Our Hospice nurses have a great understanding of the problems and needs of patients with life limiting diseases, and many have specialist training and qualifications.

If patients are low dependency, we can fill all our beds and the demands on staff will be continuous but may be less stressful than when most patients are high dependency. So much depends on the specific mix of patients and their needs.

The permanent medical staff who care for our patients are Dr Fiona Cooper, Medical Director and Dr Chris Pick. Both believe fervently in the Hospice philosophy of caring for the whole person and their families. Both spend up to 70% of their time on the ward with in-patients, dispensing care and palliative medicine but also often just talking and listening. Both believe that communication is very important with both patients and families. It is vital that everyone is informed of what is happening at all stages and that there are no shocks or sudden surprises. Both doctors have worked in general medicine and both prefer to work in palliative care because of the opportunity it offers to help patients achieve a good death and to palliate symptoms and control pain. Dr Pick commented to me that death is the enemy in general medicine, but it is not so in the Hospice. Some patients may have reached the point where the end is inevitable but the clinical staff's work is about giving them dignity and comfort. It is not about quantity of life but about the quality of what is left and about enabling family and friends to share this precious time with a minimum of worry. Dr Pick has recently successfully completed his diploma in palliative medicine and we congratulate him on his success. Doctors Cooper and Pick are helped on one afternoon per week by Dr John Kelly.

Our patients need a form of care which is more staff intensive than that required by hospital patients generally and Springhill's nurses and doctors provide an exemplary standard of care. Every patient has a care plan specifically geared to them. Nurses spend time not only issuing drugs and providing clinical care but in talking with patients and their families. Patients are gently persuaded to eat the Hospice Kitchen's great food but if this does not tempt a failing appetite, another solution will be found. When one man expressed a wish for a Big Mac, one of the carers got in her car and drove off to buy one for him. She brought it back and the patient was delighted. Such individual care is demonstrated in many small but important ways. Patients are often taken to the Spring Inn for a drink, if this is what they want. Carers often wheel wheelchair bound patients around the grounds in nice weather.

I was fortunate enough to speak to the relatives of several patients who had died at Springhill. Tracy Bullows, whose twin sister Julie died at the Hospice in June of 2008 calls the nursing staff *"Angels without wings"* and cannot praise them enough. This is very much her personal view as no one at the Hospice would see themselves as angels! Julie was a great Neil Diamond fan, as I am, and really wanted to see him in concert at the Manchester Evening News (MEN) Arena in 2008. The Hospice staff arranged things so that her pain was controlled and she was taken, in a wheelchair, with her oxygen supply to the MEN where she enjoyed the fabulous Concert very much. Her mother and sisters were thrilled to see her delight at the event.

Julie was at the Hospice for 12 weeks, one of the longest patient stays. During that period the Hospice staff and facilities were at the service of her family. Her twin sister, two other sisters and her mother and daughter stayed at the Hospice in the family accommodation for 11 nights and each morning the staff brought them tea and toast.

Julie had originally been frightened of going to the Hospice but she was in extreme pain. The Macmillan Nurses helped her but her pain was so bad that she was heavily sedated all the time and agreed to go into the Hospice. After a day or two she and her family realised what a haven she had found. The family spent a lot of time with Julie in Springhill and got attached to other patients. They were on first name terms with the nurses and much appreciated the fact that Julie's notes were there at all times for the family to read. Nothing was hidden and communication was excellent throughout Julie's stay.

While at the Hospice, Tracy and her sister Bev cleaned what she calls the 'acorn' tree. This is the tree of life, which has gold leaves on which the names of people and organizations who have made outstanding contributions to the Hospice are engraved. Tracey had a golden acorn made to remind her of the Hospice, she wears this all the time.

Another person who spoke frankly to me was Alan Wrigley. Nora, his wife of 52 years died at Springhill in 2007. Indeed her mother had died at the Hospice in 1991, two years after the Hospice opened. Alan says that having seen his brother die in hospital in Oldham during the New Year period of 2008 he can't begin to describe the difference between a death in a hospital and one at Springhill. The latter is so much more dignified and is surrounded by affection and genuine concern.

Nora, like Julie Burrows, spent 12 weeks in the care of Springhill. Alan spent most nights at the Hospice with her. Nora was determined not to give in and amazingly, when discharged from hospital after an operation and given only two days to live, she rallied and on entering the Hospice lived for a further 12 weeks. During that period Hospice staff made it possible for her to make a shopping expedition into Rochdale for some things she wanted and her family spent as much time with her as they wanted.

Alan has become one of our most vocal and supportive advocates. He tells everyone he meets about the Hospice and its wonderful work. He is a great fan of the kitchen as for 12 weeks he ate all his meals at Springhill, paying for lunch and dinner but being given breakfast every day. He also believes that everyone who works at Springhill goes out of their way to meet the needs of patients and their families.

From 2004 Alan has worked as a 'meeter and greeter' at B&Q at the weekends. He has managed to get his colleagues at B&Q to support his concern for Springhill. They bring in clothes and other goods for us. Alan, with the permission of his manager, collects bags of goods for us twice a week. The manager has also agreed that the Hospice may take up a collection at the store on one day each week. This generally brings in several hundred pounds. Alan keeps looking at things which he can do in support of Springhill and when we met was talking of doing a sponsored sky dive, at the age of 75! The Hospice helped him to persuade B&Q to become supporters by inviting staff and managers to a meal at the Hospice and showing them the facilities.

Alan and his granddaughter Emma come to Springhill for tea from time to time. His enthusiasm is contagious and his story very moving. Alan's activities have been reported several times in the Rochdale Observer.

Prior to meeting me, Alan had made some notes about the Hospice and his experience of it. I repeat these here exactly as he listed them for me:

- *Spent 12 weeks in Hospice (became 2nd home).*
- *They don't just look after the patient but the whole family.*
- *All staff from cleaners up to managers are helpful and friendly (nothing is too much for them).*
- *Meals to suit the person's needs.*
- *Family rooms if you wish to stay with relative.*
- *A level of care given that can't be done at home.*
- *Pleasant surroundings with some rooms having a patio and views of the gardens.*
- *Like to thank everyone involved in the Hospice.*
- *Family can eat with relative if they wish.*
- *Shouldn't have to rely on donations and charity.*

Someone else who spoke with me in detail was Derek Waddell whose wife Rhona died at Springhill in September 2008. Despite being very ill Rhona was terrified of coming to the Hospice as she had a vision of a bad old people's home, dark and gloomy and smelling of stale urine. After being cared for at home by Derek she was admitted to a hospital and was in a three-bedded ward. This she and Derek found awkward as there was a lot of noise and no privacy. Rhona had a lot on her mind and much which she wanted to discuss privately with Derek and it was difficult to do so in the hospital surroundings.

Rhona herself decided that the time had come to leave the hospital and see what the Hospice had to offer. On admission she was given Room 13 next to the sensory garden. The latter was to give Rhona, Derek and her family a lot of pleasure during her stay at Springhill.

Rhona was 45 when she discovered she had cancer. She was fit as a fiddle, slim and energetic and a very strong, determined person. She made five visits to the hospital before being diagnosed with cancer. Four different false diagnoses were made before the correct one. While still at the Hospice, Rhona asked Derek if he still wanted to get married, he did and they agreed a date for early October 2008.

Once ensconced at Springhill, Rhona realised how very wrong her earlier vision had been and much enjoyed, despite her illness, the five star hotel treatment (her description) which she received. While at the Hospice Rhona had booked a weekend at a hotel in London, so that she could spend time with her Mother. The original intention was to travel by train, but in the event, Rhona was too ill to do so. Derek drove them to London and back. The staff at Springhill located a Hospice at Clapham Common in London and made arrangements for Rhona to go there, each day of her time in London, for the necessary treatment. Derek said that anything they needed was provided willingly, it was he said *"as if we'd asked for a slice of toast"*. On leaving London, Rhona said *"I'm leaving a five star London hotel for a six star one"*.

Before she went into the hospital Derek had cared for Rhona at home. He said that during that period he was constantly on the telephone to the Hospice. It was, for him, a huge relief to have someone to talk to and to whom he could turn for advice. No matter what his query, he was helped and supported.

Rhona's illness progressed at Springhill and she became weaker. In early September he was asked by the Clinical staff to bring the date of their wedding forward because she was declining. He agonized over how to tell her but in the end presented it as a positive opportunity i.e. he told her on the Wednesday that *"we're getting married on Saturday"*. Derek's daughter and Rhona's bought her wedding dress on the eve of her wedding day. The girls were worried that she would not like it, but she did, she loved it.

Derek says that everyone at the Hospice was fantastic on the wedding day. The altar and seats for family and guests were put in the main lounge. The kitchen put on a superb buffet and the flowers were beautiful. Despite being concerned that she was too weak to cope, nursing staff did Rhona's make-up, dressed her in her wedding dress and wheeled her in her bed to the lounge for the ceremony. Amazingly Rhona rallied, made her vows in a firm tone and even joked with her family and friends. The Hospice staff were amazed at her strength and determination. Despite the circumstances of her illness the wedding was a very happy affair. Eight days later, on September 28th Rhona died at Springhill with Derek by her side. Her family had been to see her but she wanted to die alone with Derek after the others had gone. Very shortly, a few weeks after Rhona's death, Derek joined the Hospice as a volunteer. He does a shift every Sunday morning and is a standby for sudden or unexpected sessions. He says *"It's such a winning team and I want to be part of it"*. He said that the Hospice staff cared, not only for Rhona but also for him. During his two-month stay at Springhill to be with Rhona, everyone contributed, from the cleaner Millie, who used to stop to talk each morning, to the doctors and nurses who cared for Rhona and for him.

He believes that *"warmth and affection come from the walls"*. Once he had started as a volunteer he was anxious about going into Room 13 in case he was overwhelmed by sadness, instead he found there was still a lot of love in the room. Derek says that he volunteers not just for the Hospice, but for himself and that as he goes down the drive at the end of his shift he has a marvellous feeling of satisfaction that he has done something useful.

Another person with whom I spoke; John Cain had known his wife Maree for 41 years and been married to her for 36 years. When she died of pancreatic cancer five years ago, she was originally diagnosed with gallstones but a 'photo' of the head of her pancreas told a different story. She was diagnosed in September and was, unhappily, dead eight weeks later. She was, in John's words *"in and out of hospital like a yo-yo"*. Macmillan nurses helped and then someone who knew a nurse at Springhill helped them make contact with the Hospice. John and his daughter visited Springhill to find out about it but at the time Maree was not sufficiently ill to be admitted as an in-patient. Later she was offered a place but John thought she was too ill to be moved and she wanted to die at home.

Throughout Maree's illness, despite the fact that she never became an in-patient, Sister Pat Harding and the Hospice were a constant support for John. He rang numerous times for advice or to check things out and was always supported and helped. It was only after Maree died on October 20th, 2004 when John rang to tell Pat of her death that Pat arranged a meeting at which John met Sarah Lee Ford. After this meeting Springhill's support for John continued. Just a few weeks after Maree's death in October, John had joined Springhill's group of volunteers. Now, five years later, he still does a shift regularly. He says he enjoys the *"general factotum role"* very much and in particular likes to chat to patients who are well enough to do so. He says that he cannot praise the Hospice enough for what it did for him and his Maree but also for how, day-in day-out, it continues to help the people of Rochdale.

Janet Sandiford, who with her husband Ian, is a staunch supporter of Springhill Hospice has had the great misfortune to lose both her parents to cancer, her father to lung cancer and her mother to ovarian cancer.

At the age of 80, Mrs Joan Mills, Janet's mother, was diagnosed with ovarian cancer and had a hysterectomy from which she bounced back. All was well for a while but secondary growths were found. Joan was sent to the Christie Hospital for treatment but she did not want chemotherapy. However, kidney trouble meant that she entered Christies as an in-patient and while there she was given some chemotherapy which made her feel awful. So, no more was given. For 12 months Mrs Mills enjoyed a good quality of life at her home with Janet staying there during the week and her other daughter Dorothy staying at weekends.

Janet's father had died at home and her mother also wanted to do so. Christies however, warned Janet and her sister that their mother's condition would eventually become very bad with huge pain and frequent sickness. Suddenly she went off her food, which she had enjoyed for her last year. She had suffered a blockage of the bowel. Her GP came to see her and advised that she was *"ready to go to the Hospice"*.

Mrs Mills was admitted to Springhill on a Friday at teatime, Janet and her sister went back home that night but returned to the Hospice the following day and stayed there for the next week until their mother died the following Friday, exactly a week after she had been admitted.

On Joan's arrival at Springhill, Dr Fiona Cooper promised they would make her comfortable and they did. Joan had been anxious about how the Hospice would be but once she got there she relaxed and felt safe. The medical staff controlled her illness and its symptoms and staff in general reacted instantly to meet any need.

Joan had a lovely big bed and Janet and her sister stuck a range of family photographs on its foot where she could see them when ever she wanted. Her family were able to visit her at any time during her week at Springhill and they did.

Janet described the situation as one where she and her sister Dorothy were *"cocooned and cared for while they were there"*. They were enabled to be daughters, not carers and could sit holding their Mum's hand and could send for someone knowledgeable if she became agitated. Janet commented that some people think that the Hospice is a morbid/miserable place. She and her family found it to be the exact opposite to that. She told a lovely story of Cora Magerison who is a care assistant (and quite a character!) wafting by on the back of a trolley singing as she went by.

Janet said that everything was right and done well at Springhill. Everyone from Chris Webb, Chief Executive to Millie the cleaner hold, and practice, the same philosophy: everything needed is done willingly for the patient and their family. In Mrs Mills' case particular care was taken of her young great grandson when he came to visit. The only problem was the calorific value of the excellent food!

For the last couple of nights, as Joan's condition deteriorated, Hospice staff put an extra bed in her room so that her daughters could take turns in having a rest while the other sat with her. Even when Mrs Mills was not responding, staff came in to sit with her for a while. Those leaving for home would pop in and say *"night night"* before they left. It was complete and utter care from everyone and complete respect for the patient. At all times it was *"Mrs Mills"*, not the more familiar 'Joan'. The nurses always offered clear explanations to the patient and her family of everything they were going to do.

Janet said that she and her family cannot praise the Hospice and its staff highly enough. She says there are no words which adequately express her and her family's gratitude for how her mother was treated. The whole package was, she said, *"completely right"*. There was never any pressure or haste. When Mrs Mills died peacefully the family was able to stay with her as long as they wanted to.

I could only speak to a limited number of families but from those to whom I spoke I received the same messages time and time again:

"Total and complete care and concern both for the patients and their family"

"All staff subscribing to and practising the Hospice philosophy"

"The beauty of the surroundings"

"The willingness of everyone to go beyond the obvious"

"Care for all aspects of patient needs – social, human and emotional as well as physical"

"The excellence of the food"

"The lack of restrictive regimes and constraints".

My sincere thanks go to all those individuals who spoke to me so frankly and movingly of their experiences at Springhill. As a Trustee it was wonderful to hear, unprompted, from those we serve that we are getting it right and that every day the care we provide means so much for patients and their families.

There are many other moving and inspiring stories concerning our patients. Above all, Hospice staff try to be flexible in meeting needs. One young woman patient had two very little children aged two and five. Her husband brought them in every evening during his wife's stay so that she and the babies could have a bath together. Chris Webb, the CE says *"We're happy to bend the rules and will try anything which is not illegal"*. One lady really did not want to be taken home in an ambulance. This was very important to her so Springhill swung into action and would have had a steward take her home by car if the taxi had refused to take her oxygen equipment.

Stories of support for patients abound, even from the early days. During a concert at the Hospice the musicians and singers congregated around the bed of a very ill Spanish lady and serenaded her with Spanish songs to her delight and the great pleasure of everyone else.

Our patients are very human people experiencing real problems at a difficult point in their lives. Springhill staff, both clinical and support will pull out all the stops to help patients and their families. There is much joy in helping our patients and everyone willingly goes the extra mile.

Several weddings and civil partnerships have been celebrated in the lounge where the participants have been surrounded by the love and affection of family and friends. Even Arnie our gorgeous cat brings great pleasure to those whom he 'honours' with a cuddle or snuggle. One family member said *"Arnie came onto Dad's bed and kept him company in his last hours, something which he, as a cat lover, would have greatly appreciated"*.

Every Christmas the Salvation Army band plays a lovely carol concert in the patients' lounge. This is a very happy event and much enjoyed by patients and staff who join in the singing.

One 80 year old patient who lives alone had a very happy experience while at Springhill. In addition to her clinical treatment she also experienced the complementary therapies of Reiki and massage. This lady would never have thought to seek out this experience for herself but thoroughly enjoyed it when it was provided by Springhill. Many patients avail themselves of our range of complementary therapies. On a practical level, there is a hairdresser who works daily at the Hospice. Being ill is one thing, looking less than one's best is another and the Hospice realises very well the importance of hairdressing, make-up and manicures in aiding self-esteem.

The in-patient area is very attractive, carpet covers the floor despite the extra work it creates. We are determined that the physical environment is as attractive as possible. Yes, equipment, hospital beds and piped oxygen are needed by our in-patients but, as far as possible, those are provided in a home like, well lit and attractive environment. Single patient rooms lead onto lovely patio areas which contain planters and flowers. All but two beds look out on to the well maintained garden and grounds. It is lovely to see patients and their families and friends sitting outside in fine weather enjoying the gardens. The ability to move around and sit in the garden and on the patio contributes generally to patients' comfort and choice. It also adds to the home-like atmosphere of Springhill. There is nothing shoddy or make do about Springhill Hospice.

Our two permanent doctors work normal day time hours but our patients' needs are met during night time hours by the generous help of local GPs who offer an on-call service when needed. Our nurses work day and night shifts so there is nursing support 24/7. Day staff rotate onto night duty to ensure coverage. Sister Ann Gray, the senior nurse has a team comprising two Advanced Nurse

Practitioners and a range of other nursing grades. These are supported by a number of carers who not only provide hands-on nursing care but help with general patient care such as hygiene and showering. They also help with stock and some general duties. Nurses and carers can and often do become very close to patients and their families. Sometimes, however, families have difficulties with relationships. Unfortunately we have some divided families, some reconcile at the time of the relative's illness, others do not. Nursing staff can find themselves faced with contradictory 'instructions' about, for example, who is allowed to visit and who is not. The Hospice welcomes all visitors at any time but staff sometimes have to be very diplomatic in meeting conflicting family requirements and instructions. They do this with great tact and concern for the patient and their family.

When recruiting nurses, Springhill looks for that 'special something', a particular attitude and aptitude which some, otherwise very efficient, nurses do not have. Some nurses cannot deal regularly with death and dying. In addition to wanting this 'special something' in nurses we also look for it in the carers we recruit. The passion for palliative care which we need shows through at interviews. One particular skill which our nurses and carers need is the ability to move quickly from the sadness caused by a patient's death to the more positive approach needed when dealing with new patients. This can place real demands on our nurses but somehow, like the true professionals they are, they manage the transformation smoothly.

Our nursing team is superb, all bring something special to their work with patients and their families and all work well together. We have a very successful and effective team of whom we are justly proud. The care we offer patients is basic hands-on care and not very high tech. There is little major equipment but personal care in terms of daily baths/showers, and care of hair and nails is provided for all patients. Sister Ann Gray says *If the nurses are sitting talking to patients they are working"*. Our carers also work with patients, for example helping them to eat, bringing them cups of tea, helping with hair and hygiene and sometimes just sitting talking with them.

At Springhill we do not rush people, either patients or family members. We take time to help patients eat, we take time to talk to them and to get to know them and their fears/needs. We sit with a dying patient as long as necessary. After a patient dies the family can stay as long as they wish. Sister Ann Gray, says *"It's about the time we give people, that's important, we never rush"*. Hospice care continues until the undertaker comes, we offer dignity and respect right to the very end. Deceased patients are dressed in their own clothes. Battery operated lights are placed near the bed (candles cannot be used because of the oxygen supply). Nurses even place a little posy on the pillow. Genuine affection permeates all contacts with deceased patients. We will do whatever they and the family want.

Our clinical team has a range of working relationships with colleagues outside the Hospice. They work and liaise with:

- District Nurses
- Social Services
- Dieticians
- Macmillan nurses
- Physiotherapists
- Occupational Therapists

Day care patients generally attend Springhill's Day Hospice, a lovely light filled room looking onto the gardens, on one day a week, Monday to Thursday inclusive. Some patients may attend Day Hospice on several days of the week if their needs make this appropriate. Patients can choose from an all women group, an all men group or mixed groups. Day patients are technically under the care of their General Practitioners whereas the in-patients are under the care of the Hospice's Medical Director, Dr Fiona Cooper and the second Hospice doctor, Dr Chris Pick. However, one or the other of the doctors visits the Day Hospice each day to offer and provide any necessary medical support. This could be needed if, for example, a day patient has so many appointments e.g. Christies, that they have difficulty getting to their own GP. Our doctors are helped by Dr John Kelly on one afternoon per week. The doctors find it is useful to meet day patients as some of them will go on to be in-patients and then a good relationship will have already been established via contact in Day Hospice.

I was lucky enough to be able to spend a morning with one group of women day patients in the unit. I spent several hours with Dorothy, Karen, Susan and Judith. These four women were of different ages, backgrounds and occupations, only one thing united them – that is cancer. Three of the four had suffered from cancer twice. They had formed an amazingly strong friendship, having met at Day Hospice. I don't know what I expected when I met the group, but what I did not expect was the strong, if somewhat mordant, humour and the level of laughter. Wry jokes abounded, genuine laughter lightened the discussion. It was very affecting to hear these patients talk about what Day Hospice meant to them. Staff had told me many times what Springhill tries to achieve via Day Hospice sessions i.e. relaxation, social opportunities, mutual support, company for the lonely, a temporary cessation of fear and stress, a place of peace and interest. Unprompted, the four day patients confirmed that these aims were being met. One lady who had begun at Day Hospice in March 2008 said *"I don't have any friends here, I've only been here three years and am kinship fostering my grandchild so I've had to give up work. These people are now my friends"*. Other comments which gave me pause for thought included:

"When we get here, it all goes away"

"When we're here, we just get on with it"

"We can talk about what's wrong with us"

"Even if I haven't felt well, I've come and done my own thing"

"The staff are our friends, not just staff"

"You can off- load"

"It's helping each other"

"Can't fault them (the staff) at all"

"We can talk about what's wrong with us"

"We understand one another"

"A hug and a kiss when you come and when you leave".

On the day I talked to the group, the kitchen had put on a buffet lunch for the 60th birthday of another day patient. Unfortunately she had to be in hospital, but had asked the others to enjoy it on her behalf. They certainly seemed to do so.

Some day patients live alone and have little or no social life, getting together at Day Hospice not only assuages their loneliness but offers a valuable resource. Patients swap and share information on, for example, which insurance company will offer travel insurance at a normal rate. Details of the Home Front Working Scheme were shared as was much other relevant and useful information.

One theme mentioned several times by 'My' group was the impossibility of anyone who does not have cancer being able to understand the thoughts and fears of someone who does have it. I could certainly relate personally to this when remembering the four years during which my husband had suffered from Lymphoma. I was never able to understand completely what he felt and feared. One telling comment from the group was *"Everything changes when you have cancer – only people who have it can understand"*. One Asian lady attends Day Hospice, because while her family are very supportive they don't understand *"what's going on in her head"*.

One touching point made was that the group had such confidence in each other and their mutual support that they are comfortable taking off wigs and head coverings in each other's company. I think only someone who has lost all their hair can appreciate what a blow this is to self-esteem. I remember that my husband Doug, by no means a vain man, was more shocked and dismayed by losing his thick crop of hair than I could ever have imagined. So I can only begin to understand what it means to any woman when this horror occurs. There can surely be no greater testament to mutual trust than to appear bare headed in others' company when one's hair has fallen out.

There were some serious and moving views shared during our discussions. These included a clearly expressed fear of dying at home because of the upset it will cause family and partner. The most frightening thing of all, I heard was *"not knowing what is happening"*. The fear is well appreciated by Springhill's clinical staff who work very hard to keep patients and their families informed at all stages. One comment which really registered with me was:

"We've got this hovering over us; we don't know when we will go".

All four patients were united in their praise for and enjoyment of the craft room, built during the last extension to Springhill, and the work done by Anwen Maitland the Diversional Therapist. They proudly showed me things which they were making with her guidance; they were lovely and innovative and included pretty memory boxes and picture frames. The comment was made *"We congregate in craft; she's taught us so much"*. Another patient comment reported in the 2008 Annual Report said *"Doing arts and crafts is very therapeutic. It takes our mind off our illness and stimulates the brain. It's lovely to spend time to socialize and then, at the end of it, take something home you've made"*.

Our discussion ended when the drinks trolley arrived and my four new friends had a pre-lunch drink. I left Day Hospice feeling humble but awed by what the human spirit can achieve in the face of great pressure and adversity. I had really seen the Hospice philosophy exemplified by four ordinary but extraordinarily courageous women who admitted their fears but enhanced each other's lives.

In addition to the social, emotional and personal support offered by Day Hospice, clinical care is available for those patients who need it. One of our doctors visits each Day Hospice session and nursing care is available at all times led by Sister Pat Harding.

Anyone who fears the Hospice as a place of death would feel differently if they had the wonderful opportunity afforded me of talking to families of in-patients who died at Springhill and to the indomitable Dorothy, Karen, Susan and Judith. I am reminded of what someone described to me as a huge benefit of the Hospice's work. It was, they said, giving relatives the right to be a son, a spouse, a partner or a parent rather than a carer or nurse. Another recurring theme was that the importance of hope is indescribable, the Hospice never takes away hope. Another service offered by Springhill is the 24 hour help line. This was set up a few years ago, with a Primary Care Trust (PCT) grant. Evaluation of the first year of operation proved that the help line was a very successful initiative. Special training was provided for nursing staff to enable them to answer queries received by telephone. The service is available to patients, families and friends, District Nurses and other clinical staff.

The help line is designed to provide assistance outside of 'normal' work hours. Interestingly enough, the out of hours' period is 75% of a week. Prior to the instigation of the help line little advice or support was available 'out of hours'. Since it was established we have had calls at all times from a range of people. Our help line service differs from most in that we normally call back to make sure that the caller is O.K. Calls are made to the Help line by professionals, family members and carers. Feedback from users indicates clearly that callers value the existence of the support at an appropriate time and that the ability to talk to someone when they need to do so is very much appreciated.

In addition to the in-patient ward and Day Hospice we also offer some out-patient coverage. Out-patients can be people still under the care of their GP who require a treatment which Springhill can provide or may be people who have spent time in the ward before going home who return to us for further treatment on occasion.

Our latest venture is to have begun exploring the possible provision of Hospice at Home where Hospice services would be provided in patients' homes, thus extending choice for patients and their families. We are only at the beginning with this and consultation continues. It will be sometime before a decision can be reached on whether or not this will be possible.

In researching this book I met a lot of people and read a lot of material. One booklet 'Somebody said that word' (Living in a Hospice), edited by Christine Gittens, was published at Springhill in 1991. In it a number of people talked about the concerns they had about their illness and about what the Hospice meant to them. Others talked of their connection with Springhill. I found a huge similarity between what was said and hoped in 1991 and what is said and done in 2009. For example Dr 'Bob' Gartside who was the first Hospice Doctor said

"The first thing that the patients here need, I think, is some understanding. They often need time. They need to be able to talk, to relate to the staff that they are being cared for by. They do not want to be patronized. Some don't want to talk at all about what's wrong with them. Some are very keen to be able to talk about what's wrong with them

and have someone who's willing to listen, without the emotional barriers you get amongst your own family".

He also said:

"If, when a life has to finish, it can finish in a dignified, stress free and comfortable way, then I feel that is a very useful thing. I do not feel we have been of no use just because a patient dies".

Mrs Kay Scott, the Hospice's first Matron described, in the book, the death of a friend from cancer:

"She deteriorated. In fact I nursed her on the ward when she died. It was so noisy and we felt inadequate. You could not talk to them as a family and once she had died, the family had to go away. We had to battle with the doctors, trying to get them to give correct medication to give the symptom relief that the patients needed. It was a great strain. They're (the doctors) worried about the ethics of giving too high a dosage, therefore the patients have a lot of pain and distressing symptoms which could be relieved with higher dosages".

This experience and many others during her work gave Mrs Scott a real desire to work in a field where for a long time she thought there were inadequacies. She joined Springhill and brought to life a regime and philosophy which made those inadequacies part of history for the people of Rochdale.

The beliefs and feelings of Dr Gartside and Mrs Scott together with those of the Trustees exemplified the philosophy of Hospice and laid the solid foundation for the care and support which today informs all aspects of Springhill's work with patients and their families.

Our patients are our only reason for being. At Springhill everything we do is geared to ensuring the comfort and care of patients and their families. Everyone who works at the Hospice subscribes to this belief and brings it to life day-by-day, week-by-week.

4. WHAT WE DO, AND HOW WE DO IT

What we do is to provide palliative care for patients with life limiting, life threatening diseases at the end of their lives. We do this in the Hospice in-patient unit, the Day Hospice and also in patients' homes. Everything we do is driven by our patients and their needs. In 1990 the World Health Organization defined palliative care as follows. *"Palliative care is the active total care of patients whose disease is not responsive to curative treatment, control of pain, of other symptoms and of psychological, social and spiritual problems is paramount."* The goal of palliative care is to achieve the best possible quality of life for patients and their families. Many aspects of palliative care are also applicable earlier in the course of an illness, in conjunction with anti-cancer treatment.

What we do is simply explained but doing it is a complex business.

The Hospice is like an iceberg. The visible service provided to patients and families is supported by a lot of activity, some of which is not always visible.

The Hospice Iceberg

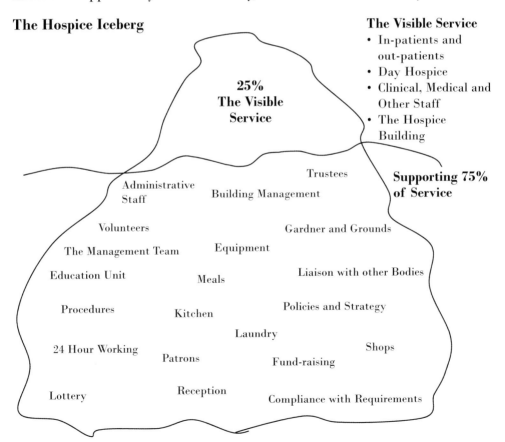

The Visible Service
- In-patients and out-patients
- Day Hospice
- Clinical, Medical and Other Staff
- The Hospice Building

25%
The Visible Service

Trustees

Supporting 75% of Service

Administrative Staff
Building Management
Volunteers
Gardner and Grounds
The Management Team
Equipment
Education Unit
Liaison with other Bodies
Meals
Procedures
Policies and Strategy
Kitchen
24 Hour Working
Laundry
Shops
Patrons
Lottery
Fund-raising
Reception
Compliance with Requirements

In 2009 Springhill Hospice is not only a medium size Hospice but also a medium size business. The annual running costs are now over £2,700,000 per year. The Hospice is both a registered charity and a registered business and is therefore subject to both sets of legislation; the Companies Act and the Charities Act. Almost everything we do is subject to external controls and quality standards. Each year we are subject to a wide range of inspections. Some of these are listed later in this Section. Everything the Hospice does is covered by a piece of legislation and the Hospice has to be compliant with relevant requirements in order to protect patients, staff, volunteers and visitors and to stay in business.

Relevant legislation includes the:

- Companies Act
- Charities Act
- Health and Safety at Work Act
- Data Protection Act
- Food Hygiene Regulations.

Important as it is, legislation is, in fact, only one of the many factors which drive, shape, influence and control how Springhill Hospice provides the effective patient care and service which is its raison d'être. The influences, as the following diagram shows, are:

- legislation and regulations
- outside bodies and their requirements
- internal polices and procedures
- the skills, competence and attitude of Hospice staff and volunteers.

Influences on the Hospice Service and its Quality

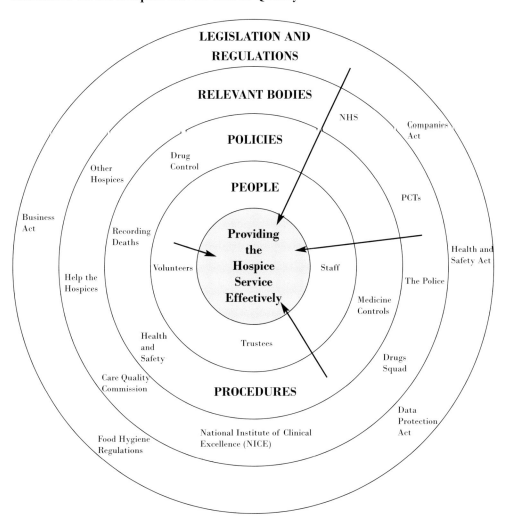

Two main drivers of our activities are the relevant legislation and regulations and the requirements and standards of the many bodies who impact on our work. These bodies include the NHS, the local Primary Care Trusts (PCTs), the National Institute of Clinical Excellence (NICE) and the Care Quality Commission.

At the broadest level the NHS influences us and our activities by its 2008 End of Life Care strategy. This strategy is designed to ensure commonality of provision in terms of the service provided to those who are at the end of their lives whether they are in a hospital, a Hospice, a care home or their own home.

Bodies such as the Primary Care Trusts (PCTs) with whom we deal and the Care Quality Commission, make demands on us and our ways of managing our activities. Springhill is involved with and receives funds from four PCTs:

- Heywood, Middleton and Rochdale
- Manchester
- East Lancashire (Burnley, Pendle and Blackburn with Darwen)
- Oldham.

We have yearly contract negotiations with all four PCTs which provide us with sums of money ranging from £700,000 per year (Heywood, Middleton and Rochdale) to £9,000 per year (Oldham). In addition to the sums received from the PCTs, (together the grants meet approximately one third of our annual running costs), we can sometimes negotiate other money, for example, for lymphodema services.

The NHS, via the PCTs, requires us to provide significant levels of information on our activities and the quality of our work. Often the PCTs ask for a wider range of information than just on the activities for which they make a contribution. All the Hospice patients are NHS patients. The NHS gives good support to us, but in no way are we beholden to it, we are a voluntary Hospice. It is very much a two-way relationship. Not only do we look after NHS patients but we liaise closely with General Practitioners, Hospitals and Care Homes. The Hospice doctors give advice to Hospital doctors on palliative care and the care of those who are at the end of their lives.

All in all, our relationship with the NHS is a very good one. We work in partnership to care for patients. The information requested by the NHS is very much that which we compile anyway for our own purposes. We work hard to maintain the best possible relationship because a win-win situation is best for our patients. A large part of the role of the Chief Executive, Christine Webb, is liaising and negotiating with the PCTs and other external bodies.

Each PCT with which we deal has service level agreements (SLAs) in place for their requirements, these cover such factors as numbers of in-patients, numbers of day care patients accepted, total days' use of the Hospice. The SLAs mean clarity on both sides about what is to be provided for the allocated funding. However, we would **never** refuse to care for a needy patient because funding had run out. We would provide all necessary care services, treatment and support to the individual and their family and the finances would be sorted out later. We would not refuse a patient because of where they come from. Margaret

Geoghegan has always said *"If a patient needs a bed and we have one available, we take them in, wherever they come from"*.

The Hospice is also governed by the requirements of the National Institute for Clinical Excellence (NICE). This organization sets parameters for the internal multidisciplinary team which meets twice weekly to discuss and agree patients' treatment and care. Each patient has an individual plan of care related to their level of need and dependency. Quite clear levels of dependency are defined; they range from low to very high. The level of care required by the dependency of patients will often determine the number of in-patients we can accept.

Other regulations are relevant to us also, for example, many drugs are legitimately held at the Hospice as part of necessary treatment of both in-patients and day care patients. High levels of drugs are administered to mask pain and increase patient comfort. There are many, many regulations about the storage, access to, administration and disposal of these drugs. We have very clearly defined procedures for dealing with drugs. Also, we work closely with the drugs squad and maintain extremely high standards of security in storing and administering these drugs. When we need to dispose of excess drugs the police are present to observe the destruction of the items in question.

We have to meet the requirements of the Care Quality Commission. This is a national, Government body which oversees the registration of Health Care Bodies. It sets the legal framework for:

- Health and Safety
- Medicines
- Staff Standards
- Recording patients' deaths.

Externally driven bureaucracy has developed considerably over the years of the Hospice's existence. Meeting the regulations and requirements is a task in itself. Sometimes the management and staff feel burdened but none the less, there is a continuing **very** high level of compliance. Springhill always scores very highly in external assessments.

As an indication of the demands and controls placed on the Hospice, the table below lists the inspections which took place in 2008/2009.

Inspection Date	Inspecting Body
July 2008	J L Wild & Co. Accountants
August 08	Static Systems (Nurse Call system)
August 08	LEIA 136 Yorkshire Street
August 08	Environmental Health 22 Harehill Road
August 08	Trading Standards 425 / 455 Oldham Road
September 08	Healthcare Commission
October 08	Penlon (Medical Gases)
November 08	Protec (Fire)
November 08	LEIA 136 Yorkshire Street
December 08	Penlon (Medical Gases)
December 08	BAFE & FETA 136 Yorkshire Street
December 08	BAFE & FETA 22 Harehill Rd
January 09	Trading Standards
February 09	LEIA 136 Yorkshire Street
Feb 09	Gambling Commission Lottery office

Inspection Date	Inspecting Body
March 09	Healthcare Commission
March 09	Arjo (Hoists)
March 09	Penlon (Medical Gas)
March 09	Environmental Water Services
March 09	Protec (Fire)
March 09	PAT testing
March 09	Celcius Heating Gas Safety Checks
May 09	PAT testing – shops
May 09	NICEIC 425/7 Oldham Road
May 09	LEIA 136 Yorkshire Street
May 09	Loler 136 Yorkshire Street
May 09	NICEIC 136 Yorkshire Street
May 09	NICEIC 445 Oldham Rd

NICEIC - National Inspection Council for Electrical Installation Contracting

LEIA – Lift and Escalator Industry Association

LOLER – lifting operations and lifting equipment regulations

BAFE & FETA – British Approvals for Fire Equipment and Fire Extinguishers Trade Association

Legislation and professional standards are important drivers but they do not tell us how to do things. These instructions need to be clear and completely understood to ensure that Springhill is compliant and that staff and volunteers always work in the appropriate, correct ways. The third ring of the diagram on page 35 is 'Policies and Procedures'.

To ensure that we comply with everything relevant virtually every activity which takes place in the day-to-day running of the Hospice has a policy and procedure in place which has been agreed by the Governance sub-group and the Board. These policies and procedures range widely, from the administration of drugs to the use of mobile phones if the main phone network goes down. All staff and volunteers are made aware of the policies and procedures relevant to their work and put them into action as needed.

Despite the range of procedures in existence, internal bureaucracy is kept to a minimum so that decisions can be taken quickly. We have several sub-committees or groups whose task it is to identify what is acceptable. There are clear terms of reference for each. Policies and procedures are designed to reflect legislative requirements, good practice and relevant professional standards, for example, the Nursing and Midwifery Council has demanding requirements. In terms of management structure the Hospice is flat. In other words there are relatively few levels of management between the Chief Executive and the people working directly with patients. This ensures that response and, when necessary, change can happen quickly.

The Hospice is often at the forefront of developments. One example of this is that in 2008 we set up a Lymphodema Service for the community, treating not just Hospice patients who suffer from this uncomfortable and unpleasant condition but patients from the wider community. The service has been much appreciated and has obviated the need for many people to travel further afield to hospitals for treatment. The Lymphodema clinic will continue in operation as it is now financially supported by the local PCT.

The Hospice is a complex business. In addition to medical and nursing care of both in-patients and day patients the management team is responsible for a budget of over £2,700,000 per year. Managers have to oversee all the complexities of the business, these include:

- staff in a range of activities and over a 24 hour, seven day period each week
- volunteers, over 250 at Springhill, over seven days per week and 9am to 9pm daily and a further 109 volunteers in the shops covering shop opening hours

- visitors (no time restrictions)
- looking after families and carers who are often upset and in need of comfort
- a busy catering business which provides food at all times for patients and at appropriate times for volunteers, staff and visitors
- hotel services
- gardening
- building management, maintenance and decoration
- fund-raising, including six shops and the Lottery
- meeting statutory and specialist requirements
- education
- Retail services.

Patients are at the core of the Hospice's business, in fact the patients are the **only** reason for the continuing existence of the Hospice. The Management task is that of allocating resources and services across the spectrum of need, within budget and on time. Everyone involved in the Hospice, staff, volunteers, (except volunteers in the shops), and Trustees have to be checked by the Criminal Records Bureau (CRB), as there is a possibility of them coming in contact with vulnerable adults. These checks all have to be paid for and must be completed before individuals come on board. With an admirable business attitude the Hospice saw the widespread need for CRB checks as an opportunity to raise some funds and has set itself up as a centre for organizing these checks for other bodies.

The last influencing ring of the diagram on page 35 is that of 'people'. It is people who operate policies; bring philosophies to life and who work directly with our patients to provide care and service. It is people who make things work and happen. Springhill is particularly blessed in the people who work for it. All are dedicated to their work and bring energy, enthusiasm and commitment to their jobs and activities. Many have been with the Hospice for many years. The organization recognises the importance of its people and operates a keen policy of training and development for its own staff. As the organization and its needs change, existing staff are given opportunities to learn and develop. This is true of all staff, not just clinical and medical personnel. The Hospice recognises the value of all contributions made by staff. Induction and mandatory training such as lifting, hygiene, confidentiality and health and safety are provided for volunteers. This provision is at different times in order to inconvenience volunteers as little as possible. See Section 5, Supporting Cast for more information on training and education.

The people structure of Springhill is like that of most businesses. It is as follows:

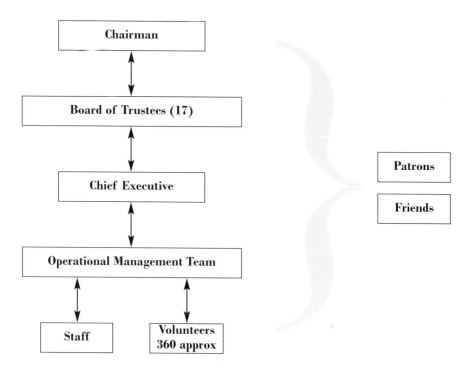

Our Chairman is Margaret Geoghegan MBE. With 25 years of office she is the longest serving Hospice chairman in the UK. Because of this, on Monday 23rd March 2009, she was presented to Her Majesty the Queen and HRH Prince Phillip at St James Palace as part of Help the Hospice celebrations. She also, on 22nd February 2009, received the Freedom of the Borough of Rochdale in a charming ceremony at Rochdale Town Hall. As early as 1988 she was awarded an MBE for services to the community. Mrs Geoghegan is a very active Chairman and remains very much up-to-date with developments and requirements affecting Springhill's operation. She chairs all board meetings and is a member of a number of sub-committees ranging from Governance to Fund-raising. She leads the Board of Trustees in determining Hospice strategy.

Our Board of Trustees consists of a range of people; men and women from the Rochdale area. These people were selected to the Board because of their skills and knowledge and the contributions they could make to the direction and success of the Hospice. They comprise doctors, accountants, solicitors, management consultants, business people and councillors and bring a very broad range of experience to their role as Trustees. The Board's role is strategic and concerned with providing leadership to the Hospice by establishing its direction and setting future aims and priorities. The role of the Board is five-fold:

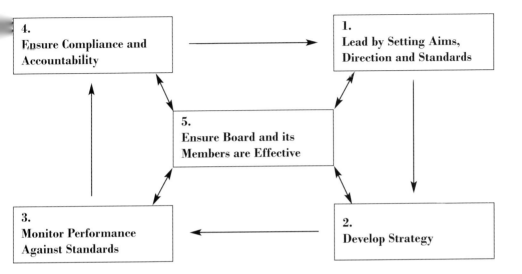

Quite clear duties are defined for the Trustees. Trustees meet regularly to discuss the strategy and direction of Springhill. Various sub groups and committees exist which use a mixture of staff and Trustees to develop ideas and solutions which will be ratified by the Board. Trustees regularly receive presentations from staff on new ideas to be explored and new issues being implemented.

The current Board of Trustees comprises:

- Mrs Margaret Geoghegan MBE (Chairman)
- Cllr Robert Clegg (Vice Chairman)
- Mr Sultan Ali (Ex Mayor of Rochdale)
- Dr Sidney Baigel
- Mrs Diane Bailey-Ginever
- Mr Stephen Beckwith
- Mr John Dafforne
- Dr Nick Dawes
- Mr Norman Frisby DL
- Mr David Greenhalgh
- Mrs Ratna Mukherjee
- Mr Eric Parker
- Mr Steven Price
- Mr John Ratcliffe
- The Right Reverend Mark Davies, Bishop of Middleton

Some of the current Board Members including Councillor Robert Clegg, John Dafforne and Steven Price have been connected with Springhill since the Hospice

Appeal was launched in 1983. Their length of service provides continuity for the Hospice. Their real understanding of the Hospice informs their decisions and the advice they give. Their length of service provides a very clear indication of their commitment.

The Board has recently been augmented by two associate Trustees. These are Ken Davis (former fund-raising director) and Ray Jones.

The Chief Executive of the Hospice is Mrs Christine Webb. She joined the Hospice when the first matron, Mrs Kay Scott left in 1996. Christine has, with her management team, built on and substantially extended the foundation established by Mrs Scott and the Trustees during the early years and has overseen the considerable development of Springhill to its current position of strength. She is very much a 'hands-on' Chief Executive who is regularly seen in all parts of the Hospice and who knows all staff and most volunteers. The latter fact is part of what makes Springhill what it is. In some Hospices the Chief Executive would have little or no contact with or acquaintence with the Volunteers. Chris' role is three-fold, firstly, to manage the Hospice through her Operational Management Team and secondly, to be the outward face of the Hospice in the formal relationships and negotiations which exist between the Hospice, the NHS, PCTs the Care Quality Commission and other relevant bodies. The third aspect of her role is PR work and fund-raising outside normal working hours. This latter can be very time consuming but Mrs Webb honours all these commitments willingly and with great humour. Her husband and daughter are always involved with Hospice activities and events; it is very much a case of three for the price of one to our great benefit.

Before joining Springhill in 1996, Chris Webb had both clinical and business experience. She trained as a nurse, a midwife and a health visitor. In 1986 she moved to a management role as Director of Quality and Nursing with the Bury and Rochdale Health Authority. It was during this period that she had significant experience of Springhill Hospice through dealing with contracts for the Hospice. During these contacts she developed a high level of admiration for the Hospice and its work and jumped at the chance of joining it as Chief Executive when the vacancy arose. It takes more than kind hearts and caring to lead and run the business which is the Hospice. It takes talent and application and a lot of hard work. Social deprivation in the area the Hospice serves puts more onus on Chris Webb and her Management Team to provide an excellent but efficient service and to demonstrate that the money donated by the people of Rochdale is wisely spent. She and her team are united in making Springhill the best there is.

When Springhill started as a Hospice the situation surrounding it and the expectations of the Hospice differed significantly from those which obtain today, late in the first decade of the 21st Century.

In the beginning it was right for the Hospice to be nursing led. Mrs Kay Scott was the Matron and was addressed as such. She managed what was very much a nurse-led service with administration at a basic level with few mechanical or technological aids. In the beginning, for example, the Hospice used a big green leather book where all patient information was hand written. Now it uses state of the art Information Technology. At first a simple Sinclair or ZX computer was introduced which took very basic patient details. The Hospice was then required to move to NHS coding of cancer. Information gathering became more demanding and the use of information technology developed to keep pace with business requirements. An IT Manager was appointed fairly early in the life of the Hospice. This was Julie Halliwell who is now Organizational Development Manager and Deputy Chief Executive.

Relationships with other areas of the Health Service have also changed and evolved over the years. In the early days relations with Primary Care Trusts (PCTs) were reasonably informal and goodwill was high. Then suddenly the PCTs were asking more and more questions, demanding a wealth of information and they became tighter with money and grants. At one time, in the early days, the Rochdale NHS Health Care Trust used to do things free for the Hospice e.g. work on heating, lighting and laundry etc. Now the Hospice has to make formal contracts and pay for such work at market rates including VAT where appropriate.

In 1996 the Hospice brought in a computerized, patient recording system called Pal Care. The system is still in use. It logs all patients' details and is a very flexible system which also operates as a communication aide. Admissions of those entering Springhill can be handled by Pal Care, as can waiting lists. Telephone calls can be logged so that a full record of contact and communication is built up and is readily accessible to anyone who needs it. Pal Care works incredibly well as a communication tool and for number crunching. Many Hospices use the system purely for the numbers function but Springhill uses more of its capabilities and sees it as a real aid to communication. It is a very open system where Hospice Managers look at the waiting list and bed occupancy each and every week day, as appropriate, make decisions or challenges in terms of admissions, continuing care and discharges. Further information technology (IT) support is available to Springhill from the engineers of the NHS department called Informatics. We have a good link with the Rochdale Informatics Team. This connection gives us low cost web and email usage in place of a slow costly dial up system where cost restricted such things as research on the web. The system also allows all ordering of supplies to be done through NHS Logistics (Since 2000). This saves the Hospice money and time because choices can be made by picking and clicking from a line menu.

The Hospice remains up-to-date on IT developments and is involved in using:

- a fund-raising database
- the Pal Care system
- the usual Microsoft Office products
- the Star Vale IT system used for the Lottery
- Staff Care, the facility to manage staff rotas is being extended.

We have a very good relationship with a local IT company: Zen Internet. Zen is extremely generous with advice and help and has given computer equipment for use in the patient/family lounge. They also assisted in setting up the Hospice web page www.springhill.org.uk

Julie Halliwell who originally joined the Hospice as IT Manager and who built up its IT capacity to the current sophisticated level, is now Deputy Chief Executive and Organizational Development Manager. This is a role with a much wider remit which looks at where the Hospice is going as an organization and which systems, IT, organizational and people, will be needed to maximize both efficiency and effectiveness and minimize cost. Her role is very much one of trouble shooting and of ensuring that the Hospice remains proactive rather than reactive thus ensuring that Springhill achieves compliance with all relevant legislation. She also spends time in trying to obtain grants for the Hospice and has had high levels of success in doing so.

One thing is interesting about how the Hospice is managed. In the organization all are equal and every contribution is deemed to be important. The Chief Executive and the management team recognise when people can be developed and opportunities are provided in order to help people reach their potential and maximize their skills. Various members of staff and the management team have and are being given opportunities to take Masters Degrees both in nursing and management areas. Current members of the Operational Management Team such as Julie Halliwell, Organizational Development Manager and Sarah Lee Ford, Support Services Manager both started with the Hospice in relatively junior roles and have followed personal development plans to equip them for their current senior and demanding roles. Teamwork really is the order of the day at Springhill.

Staff and Volunteers mix freely and work together,

It is not unusual to enter the Hospice restaurant and to see a group which consists of a doctor, a patient, a volunteer and a member of the admin or nursing staff all at one table, chatting away.

One important part of the Hospice's Management Philosophy is that 'We take but we give back'. In addition to staff development opportunities, the Hospice offers workplace opportunities for students including those with learning difficulties. We offer many such opportunities for young people who, in the main, very much enjoy working at Springhill. Some of them continue as volunteers until they go to University. One medical student, Lauren Jones, comes back to help during her holidays. There has been a mutually beneficial connection with Balderstone School since the early 1980s when students brought and prepared refreshments and then served it to the hundreds of people who came equipped with their spades for the sod cutting ceremony. In our first year, as money was tight the intention had been to close over Christmas. However, suddenly there were a lot of patient referrals and we had to stay open. We had no Christmas tree. We rang Balderstone School and asked if we could have theirs. They said yes and we had the lovely sight of a group of smiling, giggling girls carrying a decorated tree up the drive. Every year since then the school has provided us with a decorated Christmas tree, the theme of which is chosen by the pupils. There is quite a lot of competition about decorating the tree which is carried out by pupils at the Hospice. It is quite an event and enables the pupils to feel they are part of the community of Springhill.

The Core of the Hospice, physically and philosophically, is caring for patients. In Springhill itself this takes place in the in-patients unit and the Day Hospice.

The in-patients unit has facilities for 16 adult patients. At the beginning we started with 20 beds but as the years have gone by it has become clear that 16 is the optimum number to meet the local need and to ensure high standards of care. The maximum of 16 patients is accommodated in seven single rooms and three multi-occupancy bays, each of these holding up to three patients. There is some external pressure from the Care Quality Commission to move towards using only single rooms but experience at Springhill, via patient feedback, shows that, while some patients prefer the privacy of a private room, others prefer the company and activity of a three-bedded bay. With our current accommodation we can meet both types of requirement. Additionally, with some patients there is a need, for Health and Safety reasons, for them to be visible at all times so that nursing and caring staff can respond rapidly to any changes in their condition. Some patients come to us with a lot of supporting equipment, too much in many cases for the single rooms and so, these patients are best cared for in the multi-bedded bays.

Two of our 16 beds are allocated to respite care. These can be used, not just for patients with cancer, but for those with such illnesses as Parkinson's, Aids, Motor Neurone, Multiple Sclerosis and other neurological diseases or for people with serious heart conditions. The philosophy of the respite beds is to care for the patients for periods of a week or two to ensure that their 24/7 carers can have respite or a rest from their caring responsibilities. Some of these 'respite' patients return year on year. Springhill receives some NHS funding for these two beds. Cancer patients who occupy the 14 non-respite beds have varying needs and levels of dependency depending on the state of their illness.

Hospice Managers and nursing staff will, as far as is possible, meet patients' requests for a specific form of accommodation but the final choice will always be decided by treatment and access factors. Section 3 provides further information on our patients.

When the new extension to the in-patients unit was built two years ago (2006/7), two identical, twin-bedded family rooms with showers were built, the Family Suite. This was partially funded by the amazing generosity of the family of a patient who had died at the Hospice. Their generous gift was made with an expressed wish that part of it should go towards the creation of family rooms and facilities. At the same time we received a generous grant from the Co-operative Group. Together, the large sum we received enabled us, not only to build the family rooms, but also to create a large attractive lounge area for patients and family. Zen Internet of Rochdale presented the Hospice with a computer for public use in the lounge. Both the lounge and the computer are well used by patients and families.

From the outset the Appeals Committee and later the board of Trustees had determined that there would be nothing 'institutional' about the patients' area. Obviously, hospital beds and necessary equipment have to be accommodated but, as far as possible, the in-patient area more nearly resembles a 4/5 star hotel than a traditional hospital. Fabrics and colours were carefully chosen, greens, terracotta and warm oranges create a peaceful, warm and calm atmosphere. Beautiful pictures hang on the walls; these include a set especially designed and executed for the Hospice by Mrs Margaret MacDonald, a volunteer who helps each week in the Day Hospice by offering manicures and help with make-up to patients. Touchstones Gallery in Rochdale also provide us with works of art on a loan scheme. We are very grateful for this as it enhances the patient area so much.

Lovely curtains frame the windows, most of which look out onto the garden and some of which give access to patio areas or internal gardens.

Day patients are cared for in the Day Hospice which is linked to the main building.

Four Day Hospice sessions are held each week, (for a total of 64 patients) one session each day Monday to Thursday. Day Hospice has two clear objectives, one is to assist with any treatment required by the patients who choose Day Hospice rather than coming as in-patients, e.g. drugs, tests, blood transfusions etc. All this is carried out under the management of Sister Pat Harding.

The second objective of Day Hospice is to help with other aspects of patients' care e.g. social. Attendance at a Day Hospice session provides company for people who may live alone. It provides support for people with similar problems. Diversionary activities such as painting, glass painting and other craft activities provide interest and creative opportunities for patients, some of whom may never have tried such activities. The support and guidance of Anwen Maitland, our Diversional Therapist, is much appreciated as is her enthusiasm and willingness to try new things.

Also available in Day Hospice is a range of complementary therapies such as massage and reflexology. Hairdressing and advice on make-up and manicures is available for those who need it. A few Day Hospice patients attend their sessions in order to allow their permanent carers some respite from their task of caring. All Day Hospice patients enjoy the companionship provided and the food available. Dougal the lovely PAT dog who has been coming to Springhill for nine years is well liked in Day Hospice as well as in the ward.

Nobody is forced to take part in any activity in Day Hospice and individuals' needs and requirements are, as far as possible, met. Many strong friendships are formed at Day Hospice sessions and the support offered patient-to-patient is tremendous.

The next section 'Supporting Cast' describes briefly the role and work of many other people who work at or support Springhill Hospice.

5. THE SUPPORTING CAST

Everything we do at Springhill is geared to supporting our main purpose: the care and support of our patients, both in-patients and Day Hospice patients, and their families. Our two full-time doctors, Dr Fiona Cooper (Medical Director) and Dr Chris Pick, aided part-time by Dr John Kelly, are responsible for the medical treatment and symptom control of our patients. They are supported in this role by the twenty-four hour, seven day a week work of the nursing team. We are, as a Hospice, at the forefront of palliative care and pride ourselves on staying abreast of all developments affecting end of life care, but medical excellence alone is not enough. It needs the support and input of many others.

The vital work of medical and nursing staff is supported by many other people and roles. A multidisciplinary team meets regularly to discuss patient needs and care. This involves not just the medical and nursing staff but, as the name suggests, other specialities like the Admissions and Discharge Co-ordinators, the Chaplain, the Counsellor and the Diversional Therapist. In addition to this there are many other aspects which need to be managed effectively to ensure the Hospice operates efficiently. The Hospice is a medium sized business and quite a complex one in the range of activities and contributions which make up the whole.

There is a scientific theory which says that the whole is greater than the sum of the parts. This Gestalt theory is a perfect description of Springhill. There is the medical and nursing care, hotel services for patients and families, food for patients, staff and visitors, and a general administrative function. The Chaplain (for spiritual care), volunteers, a gardener, a Diversional therapist, financial services and administrative staff all contribute to the service provided at Springhill. The management of Springhill sees all contributions as equal and vital to the quality of patient care provided. All staff work together to serve the patients' interest as well as possible. This mutual respect and co-operation is the 'extra' contributory factor which ensures that the whole of Springhill Hospice is greater than the sum of its constituent parts.

This diagram attempts to explain the situation.

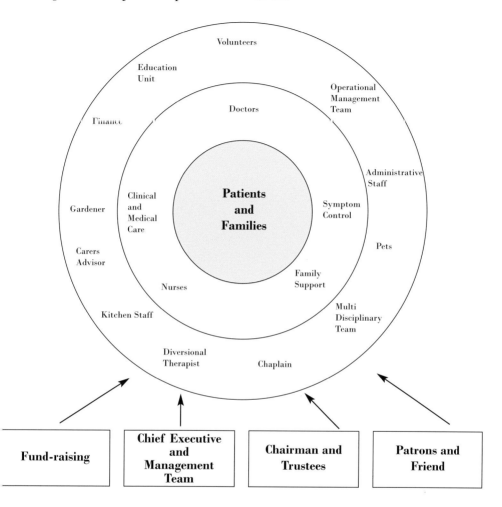

Springhill Hospice literally could not operate without its faithful group of volunteers whose activities, carried out without any charge, underpin the activities of the people who are employed and paid by the Hospice. The latter, the paid, staff number 63 full-time equivalents. All told, there are 88 people, many of whom work full-time, others who work different patterns, employed by the Hospice.

The volunteer group totals 240 or so people who work at the Hospice building in Broad Lane and 109 people who work in the various Hospice shops. Our volunteers range in age from 16 - 91 years of age and work in all areas of the Hospice. The minimum commitment which we ask for a volunteer is a four hour 'shift' (three hours from the shop volunteers). Some volunteers work more than one 'shift'. Volunteer coverage in the main Hospice runs 9am - 1pm, 1pm - 5pm, and 5pm - 9pm, seven days per week. We ask volunteers, if possible, to work their shift regularly. This enables us to plan effective coverage. Activities carried out by volunteers cover most aspects of the Hospice's operations. These include:

- Nursing Services
- Reception Duties
- Catering
- Gardening
- Charity Shops
- Lottery Collections
- Laundry

- Therapies
- Income Recording
- Ward Support
- Flower Arranging
- Fund-raising Support
- Collection of donated goods
- Day Hospice

Volunteers began to help the Hospice early in 1989. At the start, before opening day, Pat Dixon and Marion Edgson organized the advertising for, selection of and rotas for all volunteers. (At one point in our history Pat Dixon was a Hospice Trustee). The initial advertisement for volunteers resulted in over 200 people who signed-up. They put in 31,000 hours in the first year saving an estimated £100,000 in wages. The first trawl brought in 22 nurses, three physiotherapists, 32 receptionists, 14 flower arrangers, three cooks and scores of helpers. Pat Dixon and Marion Edgson continued with this job until October 1992 when they decided that they wished to be relieved of the Honorary post of Volunteers Co-ordinators. The post was advertised on a part-time basis and Mal Fidler was appointed and began at the Hospice on the 3rd November, 1992. In 1996 the task of managing the volunteers was taken over by Sarah Lee Ford who is now Support Services Manager and who still continues to manage the Volunteer Group as part of her wider responsibilities. The 109 retail volunteers who operate the Hospice shops are managed as a separate group by Dorothy Swire, the Income Services Manager. The combined activities of the volunteers now saves the Hospice an incredible £429,750 per year and literally makes possible the care and support which Springhill gives to patients and their families. (This amount is calculated on an estimate of 75,000 hours at the minimum wage of £5.73 per hour).

My own connection with the Hospice began shortly after my husband's death from cancer at the end of 1994. I became a volunteer who helped out with flower arranging on Saturday mornings and then 'graduated' to running some courses for staff and volunteers over a number of years. I really enjoyed working at the Hospice and made several strong and lasting friendships with staff and other volunteers. The friendships which result from being connected with the Hospice are often quoted as the big pay back for volunteering at Springhill, that and the ability to give something back.

Unbelievably, some of our volunteers have been with the Hospice since 1989, the year it first opened. Gladys Liddel is 91 years of age; she retired from work 21 years ago but still works in the Oldham Road shop on Saturday mornings. Kathleen Burns, who works with Mildred Sutcliffe in the Yorkshire Street shop started working as a member of an early support group and then became a volunteer. Marjorie Dent, whose daughter Julie Perry is P.A. to the Chief Executive Christine Webb and the Chairman Margaret Geoghegan MBE, has been a volunteer for twenty five years. She was a member of the Balderstone Support Group during the Appeal stage and has worked as a volunteer at Peggy's shop on Oldham Road since the shop was established, to the present day. These long serving volunteers have a wealth of amusing and amazing stories to tell. One, for example, concerns the gentleman who for years called to collect donated jigsaws. He then completed all of these himself to ensure there were no missing pieces before returning them to the shop. Others concern the strange and wonderful items donated by the people of Rochdale and the strategies used to tempt people into the shops. Shop volunteers love a celebration and there have been many parties to celebrate achievements like reaching takings of £1million, or the special birthdays of volunteers. Their faithful regular attendance ensures our shops stay open and operate effectively. This of course is true of all volunteers, they are above all dependable and willing and we just could not operate without them.

At the other end of the volunteer spectrum we have a number of young people. Some of whom come to the Hospice for experience, for example for a Duke of Edinburgh Award or as a prelude to going to University. These young people often stay on as volunteers and do such good work. In May 2006 there was a recruitment campaign for volunteers. This resulted in 30 new volunteers. Of these, we were delighted that 11 were aged 16 – 20. This encouraged the Hospice to present the first 'Young Volunteer of the Year' award. The winner was 17 year old Amarnath Marthi who had worked at the Hospice for 13 months. Other young volunteers of the year were:

2007   Fozia Saeed

2008   Lauren Jones

2009   The 2009 winner was not named when this book went for publication.

The Hospice values all its volunteers and their contribution very much. We try to recognise and celebrate their contribution whenever possible. Service badges have been introduced for two years, five years, 10 years, 15 years and 20 years of service with the Hospice. These badges are handed out at a Volunteer Award Ceremony held at Broad Lane every year. Managers, staff and trustees attend to applaud the volunteers whom we value so much and to celebrate their ceaseless work for Springhill.

In 2007, at the presentation ceremony:

- 25 volunteers were presented with a two year badge
- eight with a five year badge
- 18 with a 10 year badge
- nine with a 15 year badge
- two with a 20 year badge.

Such dedication is amazing and humbling and is a tribute not just to the volunteers themselves but to the loyalty which Springhill inspires in both staff and volunteers.

The volunteers are also invited to a Christmas Party where they are served with a meal and drinks by Hospice staff and management and some Trustees. This is generally a fairly hilarious evening with a lot of fun being had by all and a lot of happy noise generated. Wine and good food is appreciated by all who attend. It is very amusing to see volunteers and managers perform abysmally at karaoke while thoroughly enjoying themselves.

Many of our volunteers have a very close connection with the Hospice because a member of their family has been a patient and they feel they want to give something back. These volunteers enjoy and actively appreciate a continuing contact with us, allied to a chance to make a practical contribution to the Hospice.

Our volunteer group is predominately female. We have a small number of male volunteers who help in the garden, do general duties or drive patients to and from Day Hospice. Some of these men have lost their wives or other members of their family to cancer and want to maintain contact with the Hospice. Recently, we have been pleased to see an increase in the number of male volunteers. There is a lot of contact between volunteers and staff and many good friendships have been established between them. The husbands and partners of shop volunteers, while not being 'volunteers' as such, help often and enormously with practical tasks such as putting up shelves, painting and putting plugs on. Such help is gratefully received and makes an important contribution.

1. *Spring Day, March 21st 1987. Margaret Geoghegan cuts the first sod watched by the gang of 400.*

2. *Topping out the Hospice Building by the Mayor, Councillor Ronald Taylor in 1988.*

3. The official opening of Springhill Hospice by HRH The Princess Royal, 2nd November 1989.

4. 1993 Mayor Arnold Bagnell cuts the first sod for the Day Hospice.

5. On the 3rd March 1977 Springhill is awarded the Investors in People (IiP), the first UK Hospice to receive IiP.

6. Mid 1990s, a group of Hospice Volunteers including Tommy (left) of Tommy's shop at Broad Lane.

7. Pricess Alexandra's visit in 1999 on the occasion of Springhill's 10th Anniversary.

8. April 2003, Arnie, the Hospice cat relaxing.

9. The Chapel with the 10th Anniversary window. Arnie our cat is in the foreground.

10. 2005, the beautiful Sensory Garden presented to Springhill by the local Freemasons Group.

11. Ken Davies, Rochdale Man of the Year 2006, former Director of Fundraising and Associate Trustee receives his leaf on the 'Tree of Life'.

12. *Fashion Show in the Day Hospice, organized by Jackie Swire, Retail Manager.*

13. *2006, Margaret Geoghegan (left) and Chris Webb (centre) with visitors to the family extension of the In-patients' Unit.*

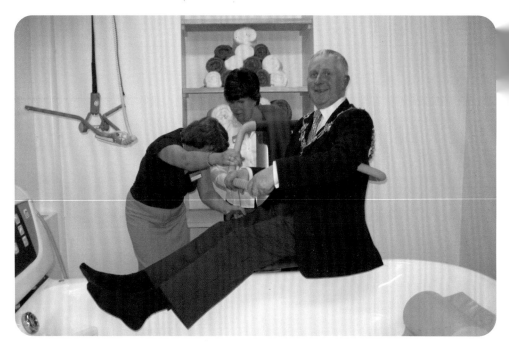

14. *2007 Councillor Ashley Dearnley being hoisted into the special Arjo Bath bought by his Mayoral Charity 2006/7 for Springhill.*

15. *November 2007. The cast of Waterloo Road meet Hospice staff and volunteers.*

Because the work of volunteers takes them into all aspects of the Hospice, mandatory induction training is provided for them three times per year. There is no doubt that our volunteers work hard and provide invaluable support for Springhill. However, every volunteer to whom I spoke said that they get as much back from their involvement as they contribute. This return includes friendship, the satisfaction of providing useful help to others, interest, and fun. A recent survey in the UK suggested that self esteem is based on a number of factors, one of which is being involved in helping others. Volunteering at Springhill certainly seems to meet this need for many people.

Although we are very fortunate with our volunteer group we need to be aware that the world is changing in ways that will impact on the availability of volunteers and possibly, on the make-up of the group.

Volunteering itself is changing as many people who would, traditionally, have been available to help have become time-poor due to working longer hours, retiring later or taking on the responsibility of grandchildren to allow the parents to continue in employment. Also, many more young people are now looking for short term volunteering opportunities to improve their educational and career opportunities.

Volunteers have played a major role in Springhill Hospice care since the first days. Many roles have evolved as our services have developed. We need to meet existing challenges and to have a robust and workable plan which will be achievable in the necessary time frame. This is being looked at as part of the work of the group looking at Hospice strategy for the next five years. Volunteers are always welcome. If you have some time to spare and feel you would enjoy being part of our team please telephone 01706 649920 (01706 68231 for retail volunteers) for an application form.

Volunteers also provide invaluable assistance in another important part of the Hospice – the kitchen. The kitchen is managed by Linda Chadwick who has been with the Hospice since day one. In fact she and Sarah Lee Ford, who is now Support Services Manager, began at Springhill on the same day, both in the kitchen. Linda has been managing the kitchen since 1996. She and her staff, including Elaine Ferguson who has been with Springhill since day one, do a marvellous job in feeding in-patients, day patients, visitors and staff every day of the year. The quality and variety of food is amazing. This quality was formally recognized in 2006 when the catering team won 'Gold' in the Healthy Food Awards. This award is presented by the Environmental Health Department to organizations which demonstrate a very high standard in nutrition, hygiene and staff training. Not only is the food varied, it is delicious. The kitchen, in addition to day-to-day work, seven days a week, 52 weeks a year also often pulls out all the stops and puts on the most marvellous and diet busting spreads for parties, meetings and celebratory events.

As someone whose husband and stepson both died of cancer I know only too well the importance of food to a cancer patient. Treatment and illness combine to strip away appetite and food needs to be very tempting to persuade cancer sufferers to eat. There is often a further problem in that patients will eat to please their family and are then ill. The kitchen staff never stop trying to meet the requirements of difficult appetites and demanding circumstances.

Kitchen staff work with nursing and care staff to tempt the fragile appetites of patients. Special dishes are prepared if necessary and meals are presented as attractively as possible. Nurses and care staff will spend time helping patients to eat. A day long snack service of hot sandwiches and other tempting light dishes operates from after breakfast to mid afternoon each weekday.

Brenda Young who works in the kitchen describes her job as 'mind blowing' with a wonderful atmosphere, lovely people and lots of job satisfaction. Brenda says she hates getting older because she knows she will have to leave the Hospice one day but threatens that she will have to be dragged out as she won't go voluntarily. Never, in 16 years with the Hospice, has she woken up and thought she did not want to go in to work, she loves it.

Even during the major refurbishment of the kitchen layout and equipment during 2008 the kitchen staff somehow, with huge good will, overcame all obstacles and continued to offer a full meal service from different rooms and even from a mobile kitchen at one point.

Kitchen staff have as much contact as possible with patients and will do anything necessary for them. In the outside world and on TV programmes, restaurant kitchens are often hot-beds of conflict and clashing egos, in many cases this leads to poor atmospheres and arguments. This situation does not often seem to be the case at Springhill. The newly refurbished kitchen now has a big hatch which opens into the dining room, when open, this enables kitchen staff to have more face-to-face contact with the range of people using the lovely restaurant and enables those who eat there to meet kitchen staff and see the conditions in which they work.

One amusing fact about the food produced by the Hospice kitchen concerns the fish and chips, which are amazingly good. The delicious fish and chips have to be served on different days each week so that all Day Hospice patients can have a chance to enjoy them irrespective of which day they attend. When fish and chips were served, as is traditional, on Fridays only, there were numerous complaints. Personally, if at the Hospice on a fish and chip day, I can never resist them.

Without the kitchen, its staff and volunteers and its great food, quality of life at the Hospice would be considerably less.

The setting of Springhill Hospice is beauplants and flowers which change with the seasons. Trees planted in the early days are now mature and provide shade and also perches for many birds. The patios and seating area abound with planters and shrubs. Little, well tended gardens are tucked into spaces between the various Hospice buildings and provide lovely but sometimes unexpected views.

In February 2006 the Hospice received a £48,000 grant from the People's Millions, part of the National Lottery. We secured this grant after a public vote on national television. The grant was for work to be done to improve the grounds at the front of the Hospice.

Nick Dent, with the help of a group of disadvantaged local children and Skill Force used this grant to complete a project which involved re-designing the car park to make it safer. Nick and the young people also developed a lovely garden and seating arrangement with a water feature near the car park. Coverage on Granada Reports was great for the young people, especially in terms of the recognition they received for their efforts. The Granada coverage also showed off the Hospice across the North West. Staff of the Hospice talk enthusiastically of the pride the young people took in the work they did and the pleasure they had in the completed projects. The young people worked effectively as a team and benefitted from being treated with respect. We saw them 'growing' before our eyes as they realised we valued them and their work.

In 2005 the local Freemasons' group, which has supported Springhill for many years, funded and presented a marvellous sensory garden to the Hospice. This is situated behind the main building and is an oasis of peace where people can enjoy the scents and colours. A small enclosed garden is situated amongst the Hospice buildings; this is called the Middleton Garden because money for it was donated from a fund in Middleton. The gardener and his volunteers maintain the grounds in superb condition. Many of the flowering plants and shrubs are grown at the Hospice. Surplus plants are potted up and sold at the Spring and Autumn Fairs and often outside the main building. They raise hundreds of pounds for Springhill. All the effort put into the grounds and gardens more than pays off. Everyone comments on the beauty of the Hospice's setting and patients, most of whose windows open onto the gardens, take great pleasure from the plants and the views available to them. There are sheltered patio areas with seats and tables around the main Hospice building where patients and their families can sit and enjoy the fresh air, the scents and sights of the gardens. One talking point in the grounds is the modernistic, brightly coloured set of 'sails' which was introduced with money from the Department of Health grant in 2007. Love them or hate them, the sails generate discussion.

The Hospice philosophy is very clear that **all** patient needs should be addressed and, as far as possible, met. One person who helps with this is Anwen Maitland who joined the Hospice in 2007 as Diversional Therapist. Her role involves her in working with those Day Hospice patients who wish to be involved in a range of creative activities. These include both art and craft options e.g. glass painting, painting, making memory boxes and photo frames and any other similar activities which day patients want to explore. The social side of Day Hospice is vitally important for the patients who attend and the creative opportunities offered by Anwen are greatly valued by day patients. It is very gratifying to see the pride and pleasure which day patients take from the pictures, frames, memory boxes and other items which they make for themselves and their families. Day patients also take great pride in making attractive items which can be sold to raise funds for the Hospice, either on Pat's bazaar, the barrow in Day Hospice, or at the Hospice Spring and Autumn Fairs. Such activities enable day patients to give something back to the Hospice, a chance they are quick to take up. The Diversional therapy provided for day patients is an important adjunct to the nursing and medical care which these patients receive. Being creative in a fun, friendly atmosphere, is a great fillip for people who are ill and anxious about their health.

Another important aspect of patient care is our Chaplain who is the Spiritual Care Co-ordinator for all patients who wish spiritual support. The first part-time Chaplain was the Revered Kevin Dunn who was appointed in 1997. The present incumbent of the post is the Reverend Martin McGonigle who joined Springhill in 2007. He works at the Hospice Monday to Thursday which means he can, as appropriate, support Day Hospice patients. The Reverend McGonigle is called the Spiritual Care Co-ordinator because he is exactly that. Our patients represent a range of faiths and none. Therefore, when required, other faith leaders come to the Hospice to help. The role of the Reverend McGonigle is like that of the Hospice i.e. it is to treat the whole person and not just the illness. His role is to give patients space to explore and express their spirituality. It is entirely the patients' choice. If someone does not want any contact or conversation they do not have to have any. Spiritual support is there if wanted but never forced on anyone. We have both a Chapel and a Prayer Room. Regular services of remembrances are held in the Chapel. As long ago as July 1989, a service of dedication was held in the Chapel before the formal opening of the Hospice.

Martin tries to introduce himself to every patient within their first two days at the Hospice and leaves with them a contact number in case they want to talk further with him. He spends time in the Day Hospice each day talking with patients as they want to. In general he finds that male patients are less willing to deal with or talk about the intangible but he tries to help as appropriate and provide the support or listening ear each individual needs. He describes quiet listening as a major part of his work at Springhill.

The Hospice is a secular organization which values all people's faith or their lack of it. As stated above it has both a Chapel and a Prayer Room in order to meet all spiritual needs and be inclusive. This is very much in line with the Hospice philosophy and its responsibility for providing hospitality which maintains the integrity of all people in the community. The 2001 census showed that 75% of the people of Rochdale identified themselves as Christians, 10% as Muslims and 15% as Atheist or of no fixed belief. The Hospice patient make-up is 1% Muslim. Some research has indicated that the Muslim community prefers the Hospice at Home Service rather than the in-patient service. We are currently exploring ways of further engaging local Muslims and other groups and of publicizing our services to this significant community.

In terms of their attitude to disease and death, Hospice patients run a full spectrum of emotion. They range from very frightened and fearful to relaxed and accepting. Martin works hard to recognise the individuality of people's faith systems and is very aware of the difference between religion and spirituality. Approximately 20% of Hospice patients will make contact with Martin. The majority of his encounters with patients involve reflective listening rather than anything else. Sometimes a patient will ask for some form of ritual which he will then try to offer personally or with the help of another local faith leader. Martin works with patients to organize and determine the order of their funeral services even when what is wanted is a non-religious ceremony. On average he is involved in one funeral every two months. 50% of these are non-religious. 25% of patients say that they want something spiritual but not *"churchified"*.

The Reverend McGonigle subscribes fully to the ethos of the Hospice that death is part of the cycle of life and that death is not a failure. He feels privileged to be invited into people's life at such a vulnerable point. He hopes to make greater use of the support of local religious leaders and is interested to see what impact a possible increase in the Hospice at Home Service would have on his work.

Much of the work of the Hospice is concerned with the families and carers of patients, both those who have cancer and those who have other debilitating diseases. The role of the carer is generally demanding and often very stressful. Springhill took part in a one-year (2008/9) pilot study which is funded by Help the Hospices and which was monitored by the University of Lancaster. The pilot study funded a new role: the post of Carers' Advisor. The purpose of the study was to determine whether there is a need for and value in offering support to carers and families. Patients have considerable support in both emotional and physical terms. There was nothing formal in place to support carers. The Carers' Adviser's role is to help carers understand what is available for them in terms of support, grants, respite and general assistance.

Another strand in the web of support offered by Springhill is the Education Unit. This separate building, called the Margaret Geoghegan Education Unit was built in 2001 with a grant from the National Lottery Community Fund. The separate Education Unit followed the use of the present board room and a small office as an informal centre for training sessions.

Training and education has always been important to Springhill, both the training needed by staff and volunteers to do their jobs, and, with a different perspective, that of contributing to the broader picture of education on Palliative Care. The first nurse tutor, Mary Kinsella was appointed in January 1993. It was with Mary whom I worked personally on the design and delivery of training programmes on such topics as managing stress and communication. I used to run these in the evenings for mixed groups of volunteers and staff. One of the groups got on so well that we continued to meet from time-to-time for social evenings and labelled ourselves *"the stress ladies"*, a source of much mirth to us and others who know us.

Jim Cunningham, Education Manager during 2008/2009 had two areas of focus. The first was the training of staff and volunteers in mandatory subjects such as Health and Safety, food hygiene, lifting etc. To be successful such potentially 'dull' subjects need to be involving and designed to be interesting. Springhill built a strong relationship with Rochdale Training Agency. The Agency worked with us to provide four days training each year on core subjects such as Health and Safety and Customer Care. Together we are still looking at ways of making training and learning at the Hospice more involving and learner centred.

In the second aspect of his role, Jim worked with Rochdale Training and the NHS Skills Academy on the early stages of an element of National Vocational Qualification which will cover palliative care. In February 2009 a four-day programme was run for 20 people on the foundations of palliative care for nursing care homes. This was well received and another programme is scheduled for

October 2009. District Nursing Services are already asking for places. Providing this opportunity for the wider health world spreads palliative care into the mainstream but also covers costs for Springhill.

The Hospice works with other specialists to raise awareness of wide reaching issues which Springhill needs to consider. These include:

- dementia and palliative care
- learning difficulties and palliative care
- consent and choice.

With the help of a sponsor we held a conference in April 2009 on Learning Disability and Palliative Care. This supported initiatives designed to ensure access to palliative care for all service users.

Our main challenge in Education is capitalizing on opportunities while minimizing spending. The Education Unit building is a major asset of the Hospice and we are exploring ways of encouraging other groups to use the facilities, for a cost of course.

To return to internal training, a smaller programme was planned which invited experts from the Primary Care Trust to present one hour sessions. This was well received. The Organizational Development Manager is looking at such issues as how a flu pandemic would affect the Hospice and its operation. Of particular concern is to work out how to transfer skills across the Hospice to cover in time of difficulty. This work began long before the swine flu situation of mid 2009 and proved very useful in a practical sense.

The Induction programme for volunteers has been carefully evaluated to ensure that it is effective in both learning and cost terms. With the present Induction programme, four Monday evenings in November 2008, 80% of those invited came. This is a high percentage when we remember that the individuals would be using their own time, and are not paid for attendance.

The programme covered:

- Introduction by Chief Executive.
- the history of Springhill
- philosophy of the modern Hospice movement
- food hygiene
- fire, health and safety

- infection control
- spirituality
- communication and confidentiality.

Comments from those attending included:

"Programme has provided me with a much deeper insight into the work of the Hospice"

"Very helpful"

"Loved how it identified our own work as volunteers and how we bring our personalities to our work".

All in all, a very successful activity. From the Hospice's point of view, training volunteers not only increases their skill and knowledge but helps to motivate volunteers by increasing work satisfaction. We will continue to care for our volunteers as they care for our patients and their families.

The Hospice is home for our patients when they are treated here. Like many homes, the Hospice has some pets who add charm and affection to the home-like feeling of Springhill. Our very handsome tom cat Arnie (the *"I'll be back"* cat) came to Springhill through Chris Webb's office window over six years ago. At the time he was an untamed, scruffy and bad tempered cat with little apparent charm. However, he seemed to enjoy the time he spent at Springhill and the food he was given. He settled in, having decided, as so many cats do, that this place would do for him. Several weeks into his stay with us he returned seriously injured from his roaming. It appeared that someone had slashed him. Hospice staff took Arnie to a local vet and mercifully his life was saved. The £700 bill was a nasty shock but thankfully the Cats' Protection League generously paid the bill for us.

The vet asked us to care for Arnie for a couple of weeks until a home could be found for him. Hmm, six years onwards, Arnie is now part of Hospice life. This adorable cat is now a very good natured, handsome and affectionate animal who is an important part of our work and is very much treasured by staff, our patients and visitors. He has the freedom of the Hospice apart from the kitchen and often makes his way into the in-patient area where he seems, catlike, to know the cat lovers and often snuggles down, purring, on a patient's bed. He has his favourite perches around the building and enjoys his large 'family'. When my Labrador Jasper comes to Springhill with me, Arnie retreats with dignity and I ensure that Jasper does not steal his food. Despite his original 'Tough-Guy' attitude, Arnie is a closet Softie. He pines when Chris Webb is away for more than a day or two and has to be cosseted by all and sundry!

We also have two beautiful grey cockatiels named Milly and Louis. These came from a parrot rescue society and are a great source of enjoyment to our many visitors. Their big roomy cage is by a window on a main corridor and often several people are gathered there talking to Milly and Louis. At one point we had a crazy crow which used to attack the windscreen wipers of vehicles in the Hospice car park. We were often treated to the sight of all cars parked with their wipers raised in the air to thwart the crow. It looked like something from a science fiction film.

Animals have always featured happily at Springhill. Dr Bob Gartside, our first Medical Director had two lovely black Labradors who used to accompany him regularly to the Hospice. My own two dearly loved black Labradors, Beau and Bounty (both now dead unfortunately) used to come to the Hospice with me and were great favourites. Bounty, whose snoring could rattle windows, used to lie quietly by my side at meetings, so quietly we all forgot her – until the snoring started. Both Labradors occasionally performed a useful service as, for example, on Fair days when the restaurant floor became covered with cake and biscuit crumbs. The sight of two un-leased Labradors, heads down and tails up, eagerly hoovering up crumbs as they advanced side by side across the room caused much mirth and many giggles. Beau used to like to visit the ward when I was a volunteer and was the happy recipient of many a cuddle and lots of chocolate biscuits, bliss for a Labrador! My current Labrador Jasper is welcomed by all when I take her to meetings.

The beautiful stained glass window made especially for the Hospice Chapel includes a portrait of Paddy the black and white Collie who belonged to a staff member. A lively PAT (Pets as Therapy) dog, Dougal the Yorkshire terrier visits the patient areas every week. He has done so for nine years. There is a lovely story of a blind lady stroking the wrong end!! Dougal even dresses up at Christmas. The Hospice encourages families to bring patients' dogs to visit them. We have even found a way to look after a dog for a patient who needed treatment. Dr Fiona Cooper, our Medical Director, has even gone regularly to a patient's home to feed their cat while they were an in-patient with us.

The supporting cast at Springhill is a vital adjunct to the doctors and nurses who care for our patients. The administrative staff carries out all the normal support duties. Tim Rothwell and his finance team handle all aspects of Springhill's finances from counting the cash received during the Hospice twice yearly Fairs to advising on investments. We wish Tim a long and happy retirement when he leaves us in late Autumn 2009. One interesting fact about staff at Springhill is how long they stay. Many people have been in post since the Hospice opened, not always in the same job because many people have developed and advanced. Staff loyalty to the Hospice is phenomenal and virtually everyone happily works many hours beyond their normal working week when the need arises. There are very few clock watchers, if any, at Springhill.

We also need to thank our Patrons and circle of friends. These committed individuals are always happy to give their time, talents and efforts in support of Springhill by their fund-raising, organizing and general efforts. Our patrons include: The Duchess of Norfolk, CBE, Sir Cyril Smith, Dame Mary Peters, Jeff Lawton, Charles Foster, Meg Johnson, Laura Fitzsimons, Jim Dobbin and Norman Prince.

Finally, but by no means least, great thanks are due to the administrative staff such as Jenny Sharpe and Sandra Anderton whose constant daily attention to detail is the oil which keeps the Hospice engine going.

6. EVERY PENNY COUNTS
Finance and Fund-raising

As with any business or indeed any individual, finance is important to Springhill Hospice. Without funds the Hospice could not continue to provide the invaluable care and service from which people with cancer and other life limiting diseases have benefited across the Borough over the last 20 years. When the Hospice opened to patients in 1989 it was almost on a wing and a prayer. We had funds only for three months' operating costs. Yearly running costs were then £500,000 and at that point we received no support from the Government or the NHS. Miraculously and with the never-ending support of the people of Rochdale and a great deal of hard work, sufficient funds continued to be raised and are still raised to the present day despite the constantly rising cost of operating the Hospice.

Today it costs over £2.7 million pounds per year to run the Hospice, with a daily cost of £6,500 or £5.00 per minute. We now receive 30% of our funding from the four local Primary Care Trusts. There are strict conditions which we have to meet to receive this funding. The majority of the massive remainder of each year's expenditure continues to be raised from and contributed by the people of Rochdale. Springhill really is the people's Hospice. Incidentally, when the Hospice opened in 1989 it was unique in that it was the only Hospice in the UK to have started without the help of 'big business'.

Inevitably, as you would expect, the cost of running the Hospice and providing its care and services has risen every year since its beginning in 1989. The figures are as follows:

Year	Running Costs per Day
1990	£630
1991	£1,325
1992	£1,461
1993	£1,750
1994	£2,000
1995	£2,250
1996	£2,400
1997	£2,500
1998	£2,900

Year	Running Costs per Day
1999	£3,164
2000	£3,430
2001	£3,660
2002	£4,060
2003	£4,424
2004	£4,490
2005/6	£5,000 (£208 per hour, £312 per bed per day)
2006	£5,233
2007	£5,615 – It now costs £2m per year to provide all our services to patients and their families
2008	£6,000
2009	£6,500

In my work as a consultant I have had contact with many organizations, in both the private and public sectors. I have never met one quite as finance conscious as Springhill Hospice. This is somewhere where every penny spent is carefully considered and reconsidered in order to ensure maximum value is received when it is spent. Nothing is wasted; every penny is made to count.

Despite this, the costs increase as shown above. This is partially because as time passes the cost of living increases but it is also because year-on-year Springhill has improved and extended the services it provides and the care it offers to patients and families. The Hospice is at the forefront of developments and is recognised as a leader in the field.

In the early days, even before the Hospice opened in 1989, fund-raising was done mainly by the formation of Support Groups throughout the district. Separate groups founded over the years included:

Rochdale	(This disbanded after about two years)
Heywood	(Disbanded in March 1990)
Whitworth	This group is still very active and raises over £2,000 per year for Springhill
Castleton	

Wardle	(Disbanded in 1991)
Littleborough	
Milnrow	(Disbanded in April 1992)
Balderstone	This became the Oldham Road Shop
Hospice 87	(Formed in 1987)

Further groups were formed as follows:

May 1990	Norden and Bamford
June 1990	Springhill 90
February 1991	Brimrod, Deeplish and Newbold
May 1991	Middleton (Disbanded after only a few months)
2003	The Springhill Crafts Group

All the support groups not only worked hard but displayed enormous ingenuity in the methods they used to raise funds. Methods included three legged pub crawls, china evenings; fashion shows; children selling unwanted toys; schools holding fun days; pub based events; coffee mornings; runs; walks; swims etc. If it might raise money one or more groups would try it. Enthusiasm never waned and the energy displayed was and continues to be incredible. Some of the original support groups still, after a quarter of a century, continue to raise funds for Springhill. There is no way to say "thank-you" adequately for such devotion. The continued success of the Hospice is, hopefully, a vindication and celebration of all the effort and loyalty displayed and a tribute to our many supporters.

The original support groups, aided by local businesses, were the chief fund-raisers of almost a million pounds over the six years of the Appeal to build and equip the original Hospice building, a magnificent achievement by any standards.

However, with an annual revenue requirement, at the beginning, of almost £500,000 to implement and provide the service it was realised early on that different and greater, more formal, fund-raising efforts were needed. In September 1989 the Hospice Trustees decided to appoint a full time fund-raiser. Mr George Kearton was appointed as the first, full time, fund-raiser for Springhill and began work in January 1990.

Mr Kearton began working with the support groups. This activity was augmented by the establishment of a number of annual fund-raising events.

Almost all of these events still continue year on year (with the addition of others). The annual events included:

- Circle of Friendship
- Collecting boxes in pubs, shops, other sites
- Calendar photo competition
- Spring and Autumn Fairs at the Hospice
- Last night of the Proms
- Woman of the Year Lunch
- Man of the Year Lunch
- House to house collections (discontinued 10 years ago)
- Town centre flag day collections
- Lights of Love ceremony at Christmas (There are now two such ceremonies, afternoon and evening)
- Children's voices for Hospice
- Design and sale of Christmas cards, diaries, calendars
- Carol Service.

From the outset George Kearton raised over £120,000 per year. In order to give him further support it was decided to institute the post of fund-raising assistant. Mrs Sylvia Diggle was appointed to take up the post in July 1992. Mrs Diggle continued to work in fund-raising for the Hospice until the early 2000s when she retired. She moved to the South West to be near her family in 2006. Unfortunately, she died of cancer a few months later. We were sorry not to be able to care for her during her illness. The early work of George Kearton and Sylvia Diggle has been continued and expanded, firstly by Ken Davis and his energetic and successful work from 1995 to 2003 and now by Ian Jenkins and his inventive and non-flagging team.

From its early days, fund-raising has become a major activity at the Hospice and is highly organized, well staffed and clearly planned. We invest a lot of time, energy and money to recoup the benefits and to maintain funds and income.

Dorothy Swire who joined the Hospice in 1996 to take responsibility for Health and Safety in the first shops later became Income Services Manager and now has responsibility for:

- the six Hospice shops, spread across the Borough – with 109 volunteers each working (approximately) a three hour shift

- the Hospice Lottery – based on Oldham Road

- the Fund-raising Team – based at Broad Lane.

Dorothy was originally asked by Mrs Geoghegan to put in a few hours a week. This very rapidly became a full time job.

Dorothy is helped in her task by Jacklyn Swire, Retail manager, David Clark, Lottery Manager and Ian Jenkins, Fund-raising Manager. If you want to contact Dorothy she is at Springhill Information Centre, 425 Oldham Road, Rochdale OL16 45Z. Telephone No: 01706 638231.

There are now six Hospice shops including Tommy's shop at the Hospice building. Tommy was the father of Mrs Kay Scott, Springhill's first Matron. The Hospice's first shop was in Yorkshire Street. Mrs Geoghegan originally arranged a free rent lease at the Wheatsheaf site. Then the Yorkshire Street Shop, owned by the Council, became available and we had an option to buy or to lease. The premises originally were in a pretty awful condition, damp and with slugs in the cellar! Nothing stopped the volunteers though. They sorted out the premises and got rid of the slugs, they accepted and sorted goods brought by the public, took donated clothes home to wash when necessary, ironed them, priced and displayed them attractively and sold them enthusiastically. Two of the original volunteers in the Yorkshire Street shop are still working there each week. Kathleen Burns and Mildred Sutcliffe, well known to many Rochdalians, contribute time every week to the shop and are responsible for a stall during the Spring and Autumn Fairs at the Hospice. Like so many volunteers and staff their service has been long, generous and inextricably linked with the continuing success of the Hospice.

The Hospice shops are at:

- 136 Yorkshire Street, Rochdale Tel: 01706 347035

- 425 Oldham Road, Rochdale Tel: 01706 638231

- 445 Oldham Road – this was originally run by the Balderstone Support Group Tel : 01706 869406

- 543 Market Street, Whitworth Tel: 01706 854563

- 22 Hare Hill Road, Littlebrough Tel: 01706 375268

- Tommy's shop at the Hospice.

There are many, many stories attached to the Hospice shops. For example the dumb waiter in the Yorkshire Street shop, used to transport stock amongst the floors of the tall narrow building is called Doris. This is in memory of Doris Cheetham, an early volunteer in the days when the shop did not open on

Tuesdays. She volunteered to keep the shop open on Tuesdays, in addition to the other days, in order to make enough money to buy and install a Dumb Waiter to ensure that volunteers did not have to carry heavy stock up and down stairs in the tall, narrow building regularly.

When the Yorkshire Street shop began there was no system of cash recording. Cash was transported in carrier bags up to the Hospice building. This situation has long been rectified and very safe and transparent systems are in place to protect and record cash made via shop sales. On the negative side, we have had collecting boxes stolen occasionally from our shops despite vigilance and the great care taken by volunteers and staff.

We have received lots of help with setting up and maintaining the shops over the years. This ranged from free occupation of the first Yorkshire Street shop to the North West Gas Board donating the kitchen fittings for this shop. Today, in many cases, the partners of shop volunteers help with decorating, putting on plugs, building shelves etc. Unfortunately, like so many other retailers, we suffer occasional damage by vandals. With typical 'we will overcome' attitudes, staff and volunteers rally round and get shops back to operating strength as quickly as possible.

When Roses' Shoe Shop in Littleborough was taken over by the Hospice in the mid 90s a large piece of asbestos pipe was found in the cellar. The official quote to remove this safely was an enormous £2,800. A friendly local builder removed it free of charge and then went on to offer further practical help at no charge. Volunteers' partners have helped, and still do so, with housekeeping and maintenance issues at all our shops. To paraphrase a popular saying *"Behind many volunteers is a handy partner"*.

When the Yorkshire Street shop opened the required 'take' for the week was defined as £600, on the first day the total taken was £687.00. Currently this shop takes £2,500 per week (keeps the Hospice open for between a third and a half a day). Until 2006 that shop was run entirely by volunteers and had no paid staff. However, changes in Health and Safety Regulations in 2006 led to the employment of a four day a week team leader.

The Whitworth shop was opened in October 2000 by Jacky Swire who is now our Retail Manager. Incidentally, the Whitworth Shop is our only rented premises. Cannily, the Hospice not only uses its shops to raise money regularly but also holds the shop premises as assets. Even with the 2009 credit crunch the shops remain a valuable asset.

The furniture shop in Oldham Road was originally taken on as an office for the ncome Support Manager. At that time we were giving donated furniture to a man who took it and 'gave' us a few pounds per year. It was quickly realised that he donated furniture was a way of bringing in money for the Hospice so we began to sell it ourselves. This is still a staple part of the business. We then went on to hire a van on one or two days a week for collections and deliveries. A part-ime steward operated the system. One of the first furniture deliveries was made by Dorothy Swire who, unbelievably, delivered a single bed in a Nova. We now have our own van which collects and delivers regularly across the Borough.

Sometimes, regretfully, we have to refuse an offer of furniture, for example when the materials used in manufacturing do not meet the fire regulations.

The range of merchandise donated by people in Rochdale is wide and varied. Sometimes strange objects appear which nobody can recognise or name. The reaction is always the same *"put it out, someone will want it and buy it"* and they do. I once bought a set of six knife rests which had not been recognised as such but were displayed with the label 'swans'. Some donations are strange if not downright awful, for example a chip pan with fat still in it or dirty nappies (really!). Others are unexpectedly valuable as, for example, when £100 in bank notes turned up in a book. The pockets of garments are always interesting, they often turn up cash. Old, unusual and valuable items are put on one side throughout the year and most years an auction of Bygones is held in the Autumn in the main Hospice building. Such auctions are run by local auctioneers Terry and Andrew Pickering from Central Auctions, with no fee and bring in thousands of pounds for the Hospice as well as delighting collectors and specialists.

Amid the general merchandise we have several speciality departments e.g. the furniture shop on Oldham Road and also the wedding boutique in the Yorkshire Street shop. This has everything from beautiful wedding gowns to glamorous Mother of the Bride outfits; all sold at most reasonable prices.

Despite the very occasional horror story, virtually everything donated is used to raise money for Springhill. Clothes, bedding, curtains, fabrics, shoes etc which are not in good enough condition to sell in the shops are carefully bagged as rags and sold to a company with which we have a contract. In 2008 bags of rags brought in £50,000 for the Hospice, enough to fund the running costs for about eight to nine days, a substantial amount resulting from items of little or no intrinsic individual value. So, all clean fabric items, clothing and shoes are welcome however used or scruffy. We like our rags. Donations can be made at all of the shops, at the Hospice itself or via the green boxes present in various parts of the Borough. The effort which people make to give to us is amazing. Not so long ago one gentleman came by bus and foot to the door at Springhill carrying a 32 piece dinner service – no small feat but willingly done. A 90 year old gentleman whose wife died at the Hospice comes every month with a box of chocolates for the in-patient area. He says he comes alive when at the Hospice.

Despite the rag provision we do receive a quantity of items which cannot be sold or used so we take things to the tip on Tuesdays and Thursdays. Regulations apply here too in that we are only allowed 18 tip units per month, so we only tip when a load is full. This means that in addition to using storage space for goods which will go on sale we also have to use space to hold goods for tipping. We get no special treatment because we are a charity.

The Hospice has two full-time Stewards, Mick Downes and Graham Taylor who work at the main building. Two other Stewards, Peter Goldbourne and David Kirk work at the shops; they collect goods in our van, make deliveries and take goods to the tip. Also, when we are able to use the charity stall in Rochdale Market they run it and sell excess bric-a- brac. This latter activity is useful in that it makes money but it also raises the profile of the Hospice and introduces it to people who may not know about it. Like everyone else at Springhill, the Stewards will do anything needed, even coming in at weekends when required to do so.

Many goods are delivered to our shops by the owners. This is most acceptable during opening hours but can create problems with vandals and thieves if bags are left outside shop premises when they are closed. So, where necessary we collect goods from homes and businesses. One volunteer, Pam Harris who supported the Hospice from the outset did a weekly pickup of bags. She only stopped doing this as she approached her 80s. If you have a contribution of goods for us but cannot deliver them during shop opening hours you can either take them to the main Hospice building or call us to arrange a collection.

Running the Hospice shops is a demanding task as there are so many issues involved. But it is a rewarding one. In 2008, the shops, including Tommy's at the Broad Lane site raised in excess of £430,000, almost 20% of our annual running costs. Dorothy Swires' ambition is that by 2010 the shops will raise £500,000 per year. Quite an achievement. As with the rest of the Hospice, the shops are not cut any slack because they are part of a charity. There are many legal requirements. There are, for example, 12 monthly electrical inspections. One of these recently revealed that the Littleborough shop requires a complete rewire. The shops are also inspected by the Environmental Authority, the Fire Services, the Health and Safety Executive and the Trade Descriptions Department.

We are now, in 2009 looking for another shop in another part of Rochdale so that we can extend the retail fund-raising activity. We are confident that if we can find appropriate premises the people of Rochdale will continue their phenomenal generosity in both donating goods and buying them. Our requirements are demanding but we feel sure we will find an appropriate premise.

The Fund-raising section of the Hospice Income Generation Department has two aims, one is to raise money, the other is to raise awareness about the Hospice amongst the population and businesses of Rochdale. Ian Jenkins, Fund-raising Manager at Springhill since 2003, says that it is a privilege to hold this position because of what the Hospice means to the people of Rochdale and the community at large. He feels there is much more personal satisfaction in working for such a highly regarded local charity than in working for a national charity which he did for five and a half years before joining Springhill. Springhill raises more money from the Rochdale area in a year than a major national charity raises from the whole of the North West of England in the same period. This demonstrates the power of a community and also the high esteem in which Rochdale holds its own Hospice. In Ian's experience of meeting Rochdale people and businesses, 99.9% of those whose life is touched by the Hospice are very firmly in favour of it and believe that it does a wonderful job.

Fund-raising is a relentless job. This is part of its attraction, those involved in it never experience two working days which are the same. The Fund-raising Team is small. Ian is the Manager, Dean Connaugton is involved in Community Fund-raising and Kath Meredith is Administrator and general support. They are helped and supported where possible by all the other staff and volunteers of the Hospice.

Fund-raising for Springhill consists of three types of activity:

- internal fund-raising i.e. carried out by staff and volunteers and at the Broad Lane venue and other Hospice venues
- internally supported or organized events and activities which take place off the Hospice premises
- third party events and activities which do not involve Hospice personnel.

Internal fund-raising comprises such activities as the Spring and Autumn Fairs and on-going fund-raising by individual departments of the Hospice, the design and production (by outsiders) of merchandise such as the Hospice calendar, Christmas cards, diaries and other items such as badges, windscreen scrapers etc.

Two Fairs are held every year, in the Spring and the Autumn. All the Hospice shops and all the Hospice departments contribute to the organization and running of the Fairs. Staff, volunteers, support groups and Trustees all get involved. Each Fair follows the same sort of layout and content.

The involvement of all departments and shops in the Fairs follows a pattern and generates a lot of friendly but supportive rivalry between both staff and volunteers.

The involvements are as follows:

- The kitchen supplies refreshments and sells cakes, mince pies, hot and cold drinks etc in the Hospice Restaurant which is, for Fair days, turned into a public café or tea shop. It also supplies snacks and drinks for staff and volunteers who run the stalls.

- The Day Hospice runs a stall which sells crafts and pretty merchandise made throughout the year by patients who attend Day Hospice Mondays to Thursdays.

- Dorothy Swire and the retail staff run a fascinating and well stocked jewellery stall.

- Linda Redfern of the Wardle Support Group runs a book stall.

- Nick Dent, the Hospice gardener runs a plant stall.

- Shirley Pickett, a volunteer, runs a homemade cake stall offering produce prepared by a number of volunteers. Her husband John is a member of our fund-raising group and also makes a mean Gaelic Coffee on Fair days.

- The Yorkshire Street shop volunteers, including long term supporters Cath and Mildred, run a new goods stall selling a wide range of merchandise which they collect throughout the year.

- A range of administration and domestic staff run the chocolate tombola, they collect suitable sweeties over months and always 'sell out'.

- The Springhill 90 group of nurses run a general tombola and a raffle.

- The Springhill Crafts group runs a stall of items created by them and their 'outworkers' for the Hospice.

- A children's activities room offering quizzes, face painting and clowns is provided. Santa visits his Grotto at Springhill for the Christmas Fair.

- Other volunteers and staff collect goods, tombola and raffle prizes, take refreshment to the stalls, collect and count cash and help out where necessary.

- Everyone helps with the huge task of clearing up after the Fairs.

Each Fair is the result of an enormous effort and co-operation, each raises an average of £7,000 - £9,000. This is a huge sum of money but in reality is only enough to cover the running costs of the Hospice for one or one and a half days. The Fairs are, however, useful for other reasons than just raising money. A lot of people have a lot of fun, both stall holders and customers. Many people have an opportunity to see the Hospice grounds and buildings and meet the Hospice personnel. Normally the Mayors of Rochdale and Whitworth visit the Fairs as do local councillors. Other guests include local MPs and the Woman and Man of the Year. Hospice Patrons and Trustees come to the Fairs and help out where possible. Hospice staff often use their own money to buy items from the fairs for use by patients on the wards, these items include such things as jigsaws and talking books. The Fairs are great events even though planning, laying out and clearing up afterwards is a huge task. As parking at the Hospice is limited, we were for many years greatly helped at each Fair by a local company, James Lewis Travel, who ran a free bus service to and from the Hospice from the car park at Springhill School. If you have not come to one of our Fairs watch out for the dates and come along. We can promise you lots of bargains.

Beside the Fairs there are on-going fund-raising activities at the Hospice itself. Day Hospice has a beautiful barrow which was donated by the Manager of the Wheatsheaf Centre and which stands in the Day Hospice. This is called Pat's Bazaar and is named after Pat Harding, the Day Hospice Sister. This barrow always contains a mixture of donated goods and crafts made at the Day Hospice sessions; these are for sale to anyone interested in buying them. They sell well. Day Hospice also does a roaring trade in very well priced hard and soft back books donated to the Hospice by keen readers.

The link corridor which joins Day Hospice and the In-patients' Unit boasts a permanent display of craft items made by Springhill Crafts Support Group. This group was set up in the mid 2000s by Maureen Styles and Christine Jones. They met as volunteers and started making craft items in the Hospice. They started selling from a coffee table in Reception. They have now become a support group which involves a group of 'outworkers' who knit, sew, design and produce a wide range of fascinating small items, most costing £1.00 which are sold, not only at the Hospice, but at external markets and sites. The group is so organized that it produces a regular newsletter. The list of items produced and sold includes 'Dammit Dolls', 'the story of the pencil', soap baskets, Easter bunnies, scarves and children's clothes and hats etc. In four years this indefatigable pair and their 'outworkers', who are helpers from among the volunteers, have raised about £70,000 for the Hospice. The group has always set out to raise money for specific requirements e.g. the soft furnishings needed when the in-patient facility was updated a couple of years ago. Other items bought with the funds they raised include an electric bed (£4,000.00), a hoist for Day Hospice, a massive £5,000 dishwasher for the kitchen, sliding windows on the original wards (£20,000). They are now working to raise £25,000 to refurbish part of the in-patient area. Their target by the end of 2010 is to have raised £100,000 (over seven years) amazing! The work of the group raises necessary funds but also, by their presence at various shopping centres and markets in the borough, keep the profile of the Hospice in the publics' eye.

Other fund-raising events organized by the internal Hospice team include:

- the yearly Woman of Rochdale lunch
- the yearly Man of Rochdale lunch
- the yearly golf day
- children's voices for Hospice Concert, held every year
- football matches
- Santa's fun run, now in its fourth year
- The ladies' midnight walk – this is now the most financially successful event, in 2008 it raised £24,000. (This sum kept the Hospice operating for about four days)
- Occasional balls and concerts.

The Annual Woman of Rochdale lunch is held at the Town Hall in the Great Room. The first such event was in 1993. The first Rochdale Woman of the Year was Mrs Charlotte Kiszko. Since then the event has gone from strength to strength and is a sell out each year. We have now got to the point where it is impossible to squeeze in a further chair, let alone another table. It is a gorgeous event where 300 or so ladies, all beautifully dressed, enjoy a great lunch, good wines and conversation and are entertained by speakers who have included Dame Mary Peters (now a patron of the Hospice), Tricia Stewart (one of the original WI calendar girls), Denise Welch (actress and presenter on Loose Women), and Graham Walton (father to the world's only all girl sextuplets). Local businesses help us each year by generously donating raffle prizes. The latter range from paintings through glass and china to beauty products and hairdressing vouchers. The lovely table flower decorations are also raffled to be borne home proudly by the lucky winners.

Rochdale Woman of the Year

Winners of the title 'Woman of the Year' have been:

YEAR	WOMAN
1993	Mrs Charlotte Kiszko
1994	Mrs Karen Hilton, MBE
1995	Mrs Maureen Cooper
1996	Mrs Karen Hoather
1997	Mrs Dorothy Greaves
1998	Mrs Nancy Todd
1999	Mrs Yvonne Noble
2000	Mrs Gladys Emerson
2001	Mrs Jill Hamnett
2002	Mrs Marjory Hawker-Bond
2003	Mrs Sheila Acton
2004	Mrs Freda Dixon
2005	Mrs Vivien Carter
2006	Mrs Carol Cadwallader
2007	Mrs Sue Rothwell
2008	Mrs Pauline Fardon
2009	Mrs Sue Verity

The Man of the Year luncheon is similarly successful and just as much enjoyed. This event is also generously supported in terms of prizes and sponsorship by local businesses.

Speakers have included Mike Harding, the Rochdale Cowboy, Duggie Brown of the Comedians, Mick Miller, Jonny Carson, Norman Prince and Martin Henfield.

Rochdale Man of the Year

Winners of the title have been:

YEAR	MAN
1993	n/a
1994	Mr Arnold Bagnall
1995	Mr Marcus Hilton, MBE
1996	Mr Joe Salt

YEAR	MAN
1997	Mr Jim Rowbotham
1998	Mr Frank Lever
1999	Mr Gerry Sullivan
2000	Mr Jack Taylor – Man of the Millennium
	Mr David Geldard – Man of the year
2001	Mr Jack Hammill
2002	Mr Fred Bowker
2003	Mr Brian Beal
2004	Mr David Grime
2005	Mr Stephen Cohen
2006	Mr Ken Davies
2007	Father Arthur Neary
2008	Mr Colin Fielding
2009	The Man of the year for 2009 was not chosen when this book went for printing.

In addition to the regular annual events the fund-raising team organize other events such as the big bike ride with 27 riders on one monster bike – quite a sight. Quite a sight also is a couple of hundred people (and one dog and a horse dressed up as a reindeer) dressed as Santa Claus and running around Hollingworth Lake. This Santa Run event grows bigger and bigger each year, lots of people have a lot of fun. This fun is a characteristic of what happens at the Hospice. There is a lot of laughter around.

'Lights of Love' which takes place at Christmas is a lovely event. Individuals and families who want to remember a loved one at Christmas can arrange to have a small card with the appropriate name placed on a Christmas tree, either at the Hospice building, at the Rochdale Shopping Centre or in Littleborough. A ceremony is then held just before Christmas at the Hospice building. So many people normally attend that in 2008 two ceremonies were held, one in the afternoon and the other in the early evening. Both were crowded. Hundreds of people attended. This is a charming event and enables Hospice staff, volunteers, patients' families and friends and others to share in the memories of families and other supporters of the Hospice.

Another fund-raising activity which is managed by the in-house team is the production of Hospice merchandise. Since the early 1990s, a Hospice Calendar has been produced each year. The pictures for the 12 months are decided via a photography competition open to anyone in the Rochdale area. Photo entries are generally on display annually in the Wheatsheaf Centre which sponsors the calendar and votes are taken for the winning photograph which graces the cover of each calendar. 12 other photographs are identified for the months of each year. All the photos are presented in the calendar as detachable postcards. Each month of the calendar is supported by a local business. The annual calendar launch is a lively event at which those who attend are brought up to date with Hospice activities and developments. The calendar is our best merchandise fund-raiser and sells well every year with copies going all over the world, as far as New Zealand.

Winners of the calendar photo competition include:

1999	Mrs Christine Pierce-Jones
2000	Adrian Carnforth
2001	Mrs M Curry
2003	Mr J Mottershead
2005	Thomas Burns
2006	Ian Baxter-Wild
2009	Maurice Healey
2010	Mrs J Powell

Other merchandise produced each year includes the Hospice Diary and a range of lovely Christmas Cards. Normally these sell out every year and are much appreciated by those who buy them. Other merchandise is produced from time to time; these items include windscreen scrapers and badges. We are constantly searching for items which will add effectively to our range of 'goodies'. We have just introduced a very useful hessian bag and an adorable white polar bear to join the existing Hospice bear.

In late 1997 the Hospice Lottery was set up. The first winner was Mrs Barbara Peace. Her cheque was presented to her at the Wheatsheaf Shopping Centre by the comedian Jimmy Cricket. The Lottery was established as a method of ensuring regular income for the Hospice. Since it was set up in 1997 the lottery has brought in almost £1m in total for the Hospice

The Lottery operation is based in Oldham Road beside the Hospice shop. It is managed by David Clark. We have a team of dedicated collectors who visit homes to collect the weekly entry fee. Some collectors are volunteers, others are paid minimal expenses. Some players pay by standing order or cheque direct to the Hospice. It is, however, always quite a task to keep numbers up and ensure that funds are raised regularly. We use all kinds of tactics to recruit: word of mouth, collectors, presence at shopping centres and garden centres. Recently, redundancies at local businesses and the general effects of the credit crunch have resulted in a diminution of player numbers. We are working hard to counter this unfortunate effect. The Lottery is subject to significant external controls and we must comply with national requirements. If you do not already support the lottery, please consider doing so, it would not only help us but give you a chance to win a significant amount of money.

Third party fund-raising sounds an odd phrase; it is simply our shorthand for events and activities organized by outside individuals, groups, businesses and teams to raise funds for Springhill. The list is endless, the innovation is mind-blowing and the activity never stops. Lorna Fitsimmons, when a Member of Parliament for Rochdale, abseiled down the Town Hall for our benefit. The Spring Inn pub near the Hospice ran endless competitions, quizzes and other fund-raising activities for the Hospice's benefit over many years. The Landlady, Mrs Carol Cadwallander was Rochdale Woman of the Year in 2006.

The spectrum of these third party activities is enormous. At one end, children raise tens of pounds by selling unwanted toys at table top sales and schools have special days for us, cubs collect and knitters knit. At the other end of the scale sits PGC Demolition, based in Heywood, which for two years, 2007 and 2008, held the 'Hard Hats for Charity' Balls on our behalf. In two fun and exciting evenings where everyone dressed up and the men wore yellow hard hats, PGC raised an astonishing £70,000 plus for Springhill. Between the two ends of the spectrum lie numerous events organized by pubs, social clubs, and voluntary organizations such as Rotary. In May 2009 the Rotary Club of Rochdale East staged a Crystal Ball with all funds going to the support of the Hospice. The ball raised £4,200 for us. Ian Sandiford, 2008/9 Chair of this Rotary Group is, with his wife Janet, whose Mother died at Springhill, a dedicated supporter of the Hospice. Various individuals who participated in the 2008 Great Manchester Run raised nearly £5,000 for us. Endless energy is expended and huge imagination displayed in the never-ending range of fund-raising events which take place as proof of Rochdale's support of and devotion to its Hospice.

Rochdale Roundtable RT55, Chairman Andrew Chadwick, generously helped with a contribution towards the cost of printing this book.

Organizations and businesses in the Rochdale area help with sponsorship for events, activities, needs and with other ways of raising money. Such sponsorship comes from organizations such as:

- Andrew Nutter who held the Nutter Crystal Ball to celebrate the restaurant's 15th Anniversary in August 2008
- Car Craft
- The Wheatsheaf Centre which sponsors the annual calendar
- Healthsure which sponsored the Women of the Year lunch for a number of years
- Barton and Kendal, Sonoco and others who sponsored the Rochdale Man of the Year event at different times
- The Shamrocks tug of war team who gave the Hospice a car
- Hopwood Hall College – Middleton Campus
- B&Q Rochdale
- Royal Bank of Scotland.

Unfortunately it is not possible to mention every sponsor or supporting organization but our heartfelt thanks go to **all** of them for their devotion, support and generosity.

The Mayors of Rochdale have taken the Hospice to their hearts on many occasions. Mayors who have adopted Springhill Hospice as their only (or one of two) charities for their Mayoral Year include:

- Councillor Norman Angus in 1984
- Councillor Arnold Bagnall in 1992
- Councillor Irene Davidson in 2001
- Councillor Lil Murphy (one of her two charities) in 2002
- Councillor Sultan Ali in 2005
- Councillor Ashley Dearnley in 2006
- Councillor Robin Parker in 2008 (one of his two charities)

The contributions made by the Mayoral Charities have been most useful in buying specific equipment and financing needed decoration etc. Such support is also invaluable in keeping the profile of Springhill high

The Mayors of Rochdale have been involved from the beginning. Robert and Hillary Stott, Mayor and Mayoress of Rochdale in 1983, the year the appeal was founded, were staunch supporters of the Hospice and today, from their home in

New Zealand, follow its progress with interest. They were neighbours of mine and one of their last actions before going to live in New Zealand was to hold a 'sale' at their home in Rochdale of items they no longer needed. This raised hundreds of pounds for Springhill.

One organization which has helped enormously over many years is Rochdale's Freemasons Group. In 2005 they funded a wonderful sensory garden in the Hospice grounds. This gives enormous pleasure to patients and their families.

The Rochdale Observer has offered huge support over many, many years for Springhill Hospice. As long ago as 1983/4 the Observer used to print lists of donations received in order to thank the givers and encourage other people to give to the original Appeal. In 2008/9 the Observer mounted its 'Spare a Minute' campaign on our behalf. The intention was to persuade people to give £5.00 – the approximate cost of supporting the Hospice for one minute. Their aim was to reach £25,000. This was reached half-way through the year and the Observer carried on, reaching an amazing £75,000 when the appeal closed. The paper's support is invaluable to us, not only in terms of money raised but also in the very important task of ensuring high visibility for the Hospice and its continuing operation. The Observer's mascot, Robbie the Bear continues to sell well and raises much needed funds for us. He travelled widely with many interesting people including Dame Mary Peters and was photographed with footballer Robinho.

Almost every member of Hospice staff, in all departments is involved in continuing fund-raising efforts. Several over the years have been involved in unusual (to say the least) activities. Cora Magerison-Williams, a care assistant at the Hospice, who started as a volunteer, has made two epic cycle journeys on behalf of the Hospice. In 2005 she cycled from one side of the USA to the other over a period of three months and. in 1993 she cycled across Australia. Together, both rides raised £4,710 for the Hospice. These two journeys deserve a book on their own. In 2008 Jacky Swire, Retail Manager, took a sponsored sky dive on behalf of Springhill. She says it was a fascinating and interesting experience but one she will not be repeating.

The fund-raising activities described so far bring in the money needed for the day-to-day running of the Hospice. When anything extra or unusual is required we have to use other tactics. At a simple level there is our 'wish list'. This lists items and 'things' which we need and is visible at the Hospice. Needs might include a camera, or a coffee table or a picture. Individuals or businesses help out by buying items on the wish list for us. We also have a drinks trolley which makes it possible for any patient who wishes to do so to have a pre meal drink. Bottles for the drinks trolley are always welcome contributions. At the other end of the scale the building has needed renovation and extension as the twenty years passed. In 2000 a Hospice Capital Appeal was launched. This was another challenge as £205,000 was needed to build an extension. This enormous sum was successfully raised and many essential improvements were implemented. Additionally, as our services progress, new and sometimes expensive equipment becomes necessary. So we need to raise extra funds to cope with these requirements.

Two other ways of possible funding exist to help us with the extra and large requirements. One is legacies kindly left to us by Rochdale people. As long ago as 1985 a legacy of £45,000 from a local woman meant that building could continue at a point when Trustees feared they might have had to mothball the building for a while and some years ago a very generous contribution from the widow of a patient contributed extensively to the building of an overnight stay room to be used by patients' families.

In 2008 a marvellous legacy of £250,000 from Mr Geoff Gardiner, who had been a great friend of the Hospice, enabled us to carry out part of a major extension and renovation to the Hospice building. The rest of the substantial work which was done was funded by the other possibility i.e. a grant. This one was for £423,225 and was received from the Department of Health. The table below lists some of the significant grants which the Hospice applied for and received over the last few years and indicates the uses to which these grants were put.

Grants Raised 2004 – 2007

2000	Lottery Board £275,462 to build an Education Unit
December 2004	Cloth workers Foundation £15,000 refurbishment
April 2004	Community Aid £700 refurbishment
May 2004	Co-op Foundation £15,000 refurbishment
July 2004	Foyle Foundation £15,000 refurbishment Rochdale Township £2,000 refurbishment Middleton Township £1,000 refurbishment Duchy of Lancaster £1,000 Anne Jane Green Trust £700 D'Oyly Carte Trust £9,000

May 2005	Links with Skillforce for Granada Action Grants £48,000 for garden and increased security of car park
November 2005	Zen Internet Free broadband for Fund-raising Department and patients
March 2006	£1,000 Manchester Guardian Trust (photocopier)
April 2007	£423,225 Dept of Health Major Refurbishment and extension of main building
December 2007	£32,800 Employment of Carers Advocate Wolfson £70,000 - Kitchen refurbishment

Receiving grants is not a right nor is it easy. It is something which is very time consuming and requires a specific set of skills which we have developed. We have made a number of applications which failed because we were not able to meet all the necessary conditions. One example of this is the first application we made to the National Lottery for funding to build the Education Unit. This application was made in the mid 1990s but was unsuccessful. It was not until 2000 that a further application to the Lottery was successful and resulted in £275,462 which enabled us to build the Education Unit next to the main building and Day Hospice extension.

Applying for grants is very demanding in terms of effort and takes a lot of time. None the less, Julie Halliwell, Organizational Development Manager puts a lot of effort into sourcing the possibilities and drafting appropriate applications. Julie has built up a great deal of skill and expertise in writing grant applications. The table above summarizes her efforts and their success!

Our final arrow in the fund-raising quiver is the collection boxes, numbered by law and recorded on a register. These boxes are in shops, offices and homes across the Borough and by collecting small change bring in £12,000 per year. Quite literally every penny counts.

The Fund-raising Department never rests on its laurels. At present it is exploring such other possibilities as selling on ebay and other forms of on-line fund-raising making use of such sites as Facebook and Twitter. The relentless task of fund-raising goes on. However, because of the generosity of the Borough, it is a hopeful rather than a hapless task.

Any ideas you may have for raising funds would be happily discussed by our creative fund-raising team. Every effort, large or small is welcome and necessary.

7. THE BUILDING

To everyone connected with the Hospice movement it is clear that 'Hospice' is a philosophy and series of values rather than a building. However, at Springhill Rochdale we are doubly fortunate in that the core Hospice philosophy is brought to life in a most beautiful setting. A custom built, attractive and convenient building set in lovely grounds and surrounded by fields, is where we operate. For all concerned: patients and their families, staff; volunteers; Trustees and visitors the building and its surroundings are part of the entity which is Rochdale's Hospice.

The original Hospice which opened in 1989 consisted of a square building with a small garden area in the centre. This building received the Rochdale Civic Award in 1989. The original building has changed somewhat since those early days. Most of the extensions have been built behind and to the side of the original building so the frontage does not look much larger today than it originally did. Many people who visit for the first time comment on how much larger the building is than it first appears. A bit like the Tardis!

At the beginning all activities: patient care; Day Hospice; reception; and administrative support took place in that smaller building, with, for example, Day Hospice taking place in the lounge rather than in specifically allocated premises. The original building rapidly became very busy and it was clear that more space was needed.

In August 1992 a special appeal was launched to raise £350,000 for a purpose built Day Hospice. At that point day care was being offered in what is now the restaurant. In August 1993, almost four years after Springhill opened, building began on the Day Hospice premises-The Springhill Suite.

The Springhill Suite comprised: Day Hospice, the Education Unit and facilities for corporate and private lettings. The building was made possible by the generosity of the Mayor's Charity (Councillor Arnold Bagnall), the Rochdale Health Authority and as ever, phenomenally generous donations from the people, businesses and organizations of Rochdale. The building was handed over on the 31st March 1994 and was open to day patients on the 30th June 1994. One interesting point about the Day Centre is that, in order to avoid paying large sums of VAT (Value Added Tax) the building had to be built completely separate from the original building. In the absence of a corridor we had to settle for umbrellas to keep people dry for a year before the link could be built. This corridor was built in November 1995. This meant that people could move comfortably, out of rain and wind, from the main building to the Day Care Centre. Sometimes one has to think that tax regulations are somewhat strange! The Duchess of Norfolk CBE, founder and chairman of Help the Hospices, formally opened the Springhill Suite (Day Hospice building). Emma Duffy, niece of Kay Scott, founding Matron, presented a bouquet to the Duchess who accepted an invitation to become a Patron of the Hospice. In October of 1997, Day Hospice care was extended to operate Monday to Thursday each week. The new addition really was up and running.

In 2000 the Hospice Capital Renewal Appeal was launched. This further challenge was to raise £205,000 to purchase new essential equipment. As was becoming the norm, Rochdale rose to this challenge, the necessary sum was raised within nine months and the necessary improvements were implemented.

Also in 2000 we made an application to the National Lottery Board for funding to build an Education Unit next to Day Hospice as the latter was becoming too small to house an active education programme as well as day patient care. The proposed Education Unit was to consist of a lecture room, a library, an IT room and two offices. In December we received a grant of £275,462 (why £62 – I don't know). The Education Unit, known today as the Margaret Geoghegan Education Unit was completed in August 2001.

By the mid 2000s the building was beginning, in places, to look in need of decoration and improved lighting. Also, new patient support facilities such as piped oxygen were needed. The planned refurbishment was to cost about £700,000. A lot of time was spent sourcing grants to help with this. We secured £15,000 from the Co-operative Charitable Foundation, £15,000 from the Foyle Foundation and £3,000 from Township funds.

In 2005 a lady whose husband died at Springhill gave a very generous donation. She wished this to be used to improve in-patient facilities. About the same time we received a grant from the Co-operative and with the combined sum a major refurbishment started. An extension consisting of three single rooms and two overnight rooms for families and friends was built. A three-bedded bay was changed to provide a lovely, well-appointed lounge for patients and their families. Zen Internet gave us a computer for the lounge.

Refurbishment continued into 2006 when we received further funds. A huge grant of £423,225 was received from the Department of Health. This was augmented by a fantastic legacy from Geoff Gardiner of £250,000. Additionally, we received a grant of £70,000 from the Wolfson Foundation. With this funding we embarked on the most ambitious of our refurbishment programmes.

This included:

- a completely remodelled reception area
- complete refurbishment of the main lounge and dining room
- a brand new kitchen – new layout and new equipment
- new lightening and carpets in all corridors
- modernization of the Chapel
- creation of a new quiet room for use by patients, families and visitors
- erection of the colourful sails feature and the creation of a new small garden area.

This splendid face-lift caused untold problems for staff as it was very much 'business as usual' while the builders were in and chaos reigned. Sarah Lee Ford, Support Services Manager, did a Trojan job of managing the enormous project and of persuading the builders to do lots of small jobs not necessarily included in the contract without charging us. Her phrase *"while you're here could you.....?"* became legendary.

The revised Hospice was formally opened in May 2006 by The Mayor, Councillor Ashley Dearnley. Mrs June Law who had contributed the first £5.00 towards the original appeal attended as did the Mayor and Mayoress and Geoff Gardiner's son.

This extensive refurbishment and the improvements it implemented has equipped us well for the next 10 to 20 years. This is fortunate in that now that times are hard, we should not need many extra funds to develop or expand the building further. Good husbandry and the Hospice's usual good financial management will enable the required maintenance to take place.

The improved building is a delightful place to be and provides a comfortable, well-equipped home for our patients and a good work place for our staff and volunteers.

When money permits we will look to extend our laundry facility and to build some outside storage. There are no further extensions to the main building planned right now, but who knows what the future will bring?

Internally Springhill is a well-decorated, attractive and pleasant place to be. Furnishings and decorations are all in first class condition. There is 'no make do and mend' here. We believe strongly that while people are ill, comfortable, pleasant surroundings reduce stress and anxiety.

There are flowers everywhere, in reception, in the corridors, in the wards, in offices and in the Day Centre. These flowers are donated to the Hospice and therefore cost us nothing. They are arranged by some of our volunteers who have a purpose built working area which was prepared for them during the recent major refurbishment. This is something they had wanted for 18 years!

Lovely pictures hang on the wall, many of these were donated, and some were made specifically for the Hospice. As art is very much a personal choice, some of the pictures cause a little discussion but the general ambience is superb.

The gardens and grounds form a major part of Springhill's attraction as anyone who walks or drives up the hill can confirm. Section 5 of the book, the Supporting Cast, describes in some detail the work of Nick Dent, our gardener and the volunteers who work with him to keep the grounds looking so marvellous. Recently Nick has designed a garden for Bury Hospice and will be selling them the plants required for his design, thereby raising more ever needed funds for Springhill.

We are actively exploring ways of using the resource which is the Education Unit to generate funds for the Hospice, for example by encouraging other bodies to use our premises in return for a fee. Not only are our buildings beautiful and very much fit for purpose, wherever possible we use them to generate funds for the Hospice. As I said in another part of this book 'every penny counts' and we are keen to make all our assets work for us.

We are justifiably proud of Rochdale's Hospice. If you have never seen it, or not seen it for some years come and visit us. Just give Reception a ring and we will arrange something for you.

I hope that this book has given you a better understanding of Rochdale's Hospice and of the affection in which it is held by Rochdalians. If you feel you could, or want to help in any way please get in touch. Contact details are given on page 113.

Diane Bailey-Ginever

Diane Bailey-Ginever
Bamford, Rochdale, August 2009

3. CONCLUSION BY CHRISTINE WEBB

In this our 20th year we wanted to celebrate the work of and the people associated with Springhill Hospice. For over 25 years we have been raising money, firstly to build a hospice and then to have enough money to run it, we have succeeded only because of the support given by the people of Rochdale for over twenty five years! What a magnificent story and success it has been.

Originally a Hospice for Rochdale hardly seemed possible, it meant a huge fund-raising effort from so many people to make the dream become a reality. But it did happen and here we are, twenty years on. We are now a thriving Hospice having cared for many thousands of people over the years, patients who needed palliative care, their families and friends.

As you will have read in the earlier chapters of the book Margaret Geoghegan, MBE, her friends and colleagues, set about the task of establishing 'A Hospice for Rochdale'. Even today some of these people remain involved in the business of being Trustees of the Hospice, overseeing the many changes and developments we have made. Margaret is as committed today, in the work we do, as she was twenty six years ago. She is interested in everything we are doing and is immensely proud of the facilities we have on offer. Steven Price, Sydney Baigel, John Dafforne and Robert Clegg all of whom have been involved from the very beginning, still support the work of Springhill on behalf of the people in our town by continuing as Hospice Trustees.

Over the years the original 20 bedded Hospice has changed, grown in many ways, new buildings and services having been developed in an effort to respond to the ever changing needs of our patients and the communities they come from. Whilst the frontage of Springhill still looks the same, the building has been added to a great deal over the years, with more single patient bedrooms, giving patients a choice of where they wish to be cared for, a single room or a three bedded ward? The opening of the Margaret Geoghegan Education Centre in 2000 which provides a wide range of skills and education training for our own staff as well as those professionals in the community and other Hospices has added great benefit to the development of specialist palliative care knowledge. We have additional therapy rooms in Day Hospice and a new kitchen and dining facilities which are state of the art. My office is in the reception area and I am able to listen to the many comments of people visiting us. There is genuine surprise at how bright and welcoming the Hospice is, but more importantly the comments about staff and volunteers being so approachable and the place being so relaxed and happy are good to hear as they further endorse the view we want to encourage here. We are fortunate to have many visitors to the Hospice, those who wish to volunteer fund-raise or those who are just interested in the Hospice and what it does.

When people have been shown around the Hospice they often say how surprised they are with the size of the building, comments often include it is much bigger than it looks from the front and how light, bright and spacious it is! We have always thought it important to respond to requests for additional services, whilst at the same time we made sure that any new building fits in with the existing facilities and looks as though it had been developed at the same time as the original part of the Hospice.

Springhill Hospice is a truly great mix of people, traditions, teamwork and hope. The people are the thing which makes the difference; lots of people from a wide range of backgrounds all working to the same target – to make a difference for the patients and families who use our services. It is always a pleasure to see the many interactions that take place each and every day. Kindnesses that are so easy to do and so willingly given and the ability for the many differences in each and every one of us to come together in a concerted way so that patients feel so well supported in the journey they are on. It has been such a privilege to be part of the development of Springhill and in helping to set the tone for the next twenty years.

Choosing the site where we now have the Hospice was a magnificent choice by the original Trustees, from 27 pieces of land the Council gave us for consideration. The Springhill site has accommodated our needs well, with the Rochdale Council providing us with additional land as our requirements changed and we needed to extend. It is clear that we have one of the most lovely, purpose built buildings, in a setting that is truly gorgeous, in the country, of course we are slightly biased!

Whilst the building is obviously important to all concerned, it is the people within the Hospice who really do make the difference. Throughout this book you will have read stories, many about the staff and volunteers who play such an enormous part in the work we carry out. However, the only reason we have staff and volunteers is because of our patients. Our task consists of meeting the constantly changing needs of patients and their families, providing care at what for most people is a time when they are most in need, at their most vulnerable and require the most highly developed skills from the professionals and volunteers caring for them. The patients really do make the work we do such a joy and without doubt we consider it an absolute privilege to work with them.

The volunteers I have met over the twelve years I have been at Springhill have been a revelation, their kindnesses, commonsense approach and total commitment to our cause are truly amazing. There are so many volunteers that I could mention individually because of the part they have played, but that would be unfair so I will just say that this Hospice is as successful as it is because of the massive part that the many volunteers we have, have played in its development. The volunteers, men and women, young and not so young turn up for their shifts with such a willingness to care; it is often moving to see them in action. The volunteers come from all walks of life and more recently we have had volunteers who have been made redundant, have lost their jobs and businesses in the world recession of which we are in the midst, but have offered their time to a good cause. Some volunteers, of course, offer their skills in Retail, Fund-raising or as Lottery collectors but all have the same aim, to help maintain the work of the Hospice so that people at the end of their lives will receive the care and support they need.

With the work we do in helping patients to manage their lives, we have identified a gap in our services, one which allows patients to choose to be cared for in their own home. The concept of Hospice at Home is a well researched and successful model and we are in the early stages of developing, alongside patients, carers, volunteers and professionals, a version that suits our patients and their families. Of course, as with any other health care business, the issue of finances does provide us with a big obstacle, however, as we have seen over the last twenty five years, this has never stopped us developing services before and I am sure this won't be the case now.

Focusing on the care we offer is very important to us all at Springhill Hospice, we only get one chance to get it right, the very nature of the dying process is we have to be certain that the care on offer is flexible, delivered sensitively by experts in their field and, of course, compassionately. Springhill Hospice strives to get the balance right, allowing patients and their families to live their lives to the full, making their own choices about what they want to happen to them and how services will be delivered and being assured that they will receive the highest standard of care from staff and volunteers.

Anyone who has visited Springhill will tell you, I am sure, that it is not a sad, gloomy or frightening place, quite the opposite in fact. It is a place that encourages people to make the most of the time they have. Patients and families are hugely resourceful and draw on the time they have to engage in much laughter and family time. As I write this piece, at the end of July 2009 the sun is shining and patients are sitting out in the sunshine on sun-loungers, under the shade of big umbrellas, enjoying the beautiful grounds, watching the bird life, chatting or just sitting and thinking; they experience no pressure to engage in anything other than that they much want to.

Our 20th year is a wonderful milestone and one in which we all share the success. The most important thing is for the legacy of the last twenty years to be carried forward, making sure our services are what is wanted by our patients, their families and of course the people in our many communities that support us in so many different ways.

So, for the future we need our staff to remain skilled in providing specialist palliative care, constantly updating their education and skills so they can deliver care in an environment that is flexible, welcoming and secure. Volunteers need to continue to be an integral part of the services we have on offer, bringing their enthusiasm, skills and passion to their area of work, they are such a valuable asset to the work we undertake and make the success of the Hospice complete.

We are fortunate that so many people in our area choose to support us in our work; we don't take this for granted for one minute, but remain proud of the partnerships and alliances that have grown over time and hope that these will grow and flourish to meet the next twenty years and what they bring for us.

Christine Webb
Chief Executive
Springhill Hospice, July 2009

PS Should you require further copies of this book they can be bought from any of our Hospice shops (see page 113 for addresses) or from Sandiford's Gallery Ltd. 78 Drake Street. Rochdale 01706646563 (card facilities are available).

9. YEAR-BY-YEAR TIMELINE 1983 – 2009

This section is not a narrative as the other sections but is a yearly summary of events from 1983 to 2009

1983

- April 15 – the constitution for the Hospice Appeal was adopted.
- May – Margaret Geoghegan launched fund-raising appeal, kicked off by £5 from a colleague, Mrs June Law.
- 8th May – public meeting in the Parish Church to launch appeal and start fund-raising.
- 4th June – Announcement made that £1,744 had been raised in the first month.
- 1983/84 – Fund-raising continued in Support Groups, shops, businesses, and the public supported by the Rochdale Observer.

1984

- 1984 – In June the target for fund-raising was £800,000 and there was £45,000 in the bank.
- 1984 – the Mayor, Councillor Norman Angus made the appeal for the Hospice his charity for his year of office 1984/85.

1985

- 1st May – Mayor of Rochdale, Councillor Norman Angus handed the Trustees the lease for the land at Broad Lane (The site chosen from 27 possibilities).

1985/1986

- Fund-raising continued as did Trustee planning and meetings.
- Design produced for the building.
- Architect Mr A Potts and builders G & J Seddon appointed.
- Health Authority 'loaned' the Hospice a team of three professionals, Mr A Potts an architect, Mr J Sunderland an engineer and Mr J Kemp a quantity surveyor.

1987

- March – Building contractor G & J Seddon moved onto the site and excavation began.

- The original site hut and plans were destroyed by vandals. Seddons paid for a watchman after this occurred.

- 21st March – Margaret Geoghegan cut the first sod aided by 400+ men women and children of Rochdale.

- Fund-raising continued.

1988

- February 1988 – the building was up, roofed and watertight. By now £600,000 had been raised towards a revised total of £900,000. Mrs Geoghegan said *"this must be the greatest fund-raising effort ever in Rochdale"*.

- June 1988 – Margaret Geoghegan was awarded the MBE for services to the Community.

- October 1988 – Kay Scott, a nursing manager from Birch Hill was appointed the first matron of Springhill Hospice.

- Late 1988 – Mrs Scott began the task of equipping the Hospice building and putting together the first team.

- December 1988 – Mrs Geoghegan formally accepted the completed building from the contractors.

1989

- February 1989 – A half ton of daffodil bulbs was given to the Hospice and planted, in the rain, on the approach to the building by a team of Scouts and Guides.

- February 1989 – An appeal for volunteers was launched and 200 were recruited.

- 2nd July 1989 – A service of dedication was held in the Hospice Chapel.

- July 1989 – Dr Robert (Bob) Gartside joined the Medical Team as part time Hospice Doctor.

- 1st October 1989 – The first two patients (both from Middleton) arrived and caring began.

- November 1989 – Princess Anne formally opened the Hospice which had 25 members of staff at that point.

1990/1991

- First full time fund-raiser, George Kearton, was appointed and began work in January 1990.
- April 1990 the Hospice received an Astra estate car for the fund-raiser.
- 6th September 1990 – First four day-care patients attended.
- Caring continued and numbers of patients increased.
- 1991 – Increase in Day Hospice, now operating Mondays and Thursdays.

1991

- March – Sponsorship raised to publish Springhillian magazine twice per year.
- August – a Borough-wide collection raised nearly £21,000 (27% up on the previous year). Hundreds collected and thousands contributed.
- 12 churches in the Borough organized a collection on Hospice Sunday 28th October and raised £1,800.
- October – Bereavement Support Group set up.

1992

- Caring continued and the Hospice consolidated its care and services.
- March – first ever Children's Voices for Hospices in the UK.
- The Mayor, Councillor Arnold Bagnall made the Hospice his mayoral charity.
- May the Ambulance service offered us a free ambulance, handed over in July 1992.
- 6th June – First ever 'Last night of the Proms' concert took place at Gracie Fields Theatre.
- Appointment of Sylvia Diggle as fund-raising assistant.
- August – Special Appeal launched to raise £350,000 for a purpose built Day Hospice (Day care was being offered in what is now the restaurant).

- October – over 200 local singers performed a wonderful evening of Gilbert and Sullivan as our 1992 Voices for Hospices event.

- Day Care Unit was now open on Mondays, Tuesday and Thursdays – 12 patients each time.

1993

- January Mary Kinsella joined as tutor/practitioner.

- April – the first Woman of Rochdale of the Year Luncheon was held, Mrs Charlotte Kiszko was chosen as woman of the year.

- The third six week course on 'The Care of the Dying' was completed. A fourth was planned for February 1993.

- August – building of the Day Centre began.

- 21st September – men's charity golf day.

- 26th November – Afternoon tea dance in the Grand Hall, Rochdale Town Hall.

- The Hospice was at this point caring for 18 in-patients and approx 30 day patients per week.

- Bereavement group now on-going.

- Appointment of Colette Rodgers – working 20 hours per week to set up and prepare a training programme for the needs of the service and the staff.

- Cora Magerison cycled across Australia to raise funds.

- £1,750 per day to keep the Hospice going (Daily cost of £100 per bed per day).

- New Board of Trustees appointed.

- Recent proposals to levy VAT on gas and electricity added £3,000 to our running costs.

- Work began on building the purpose built Day Care Unit.

1994

- Completion and opening of the Springhill Suite comprising: Day Hospice, Education Unit, facilities for corporate and private lettings. Made possible by the generosity of the Mayor's charity (Councillor Arnold Bagnall), the Rochdale Health Authority and generous dominations from the public and local organizations. Handed over 31st March 1994.

- 30th June – Day Centre open to patients.

- Care in the Community in its first year brought closer liaison with social services and Health Trusts.

- Julie Halliwell was appointed as Information Technology Manager.

- 2nd Children's Voices for Hospice.

- October – the Hospice held its first Regional Palliative Care conference.

- By end of 1994, the daily rate to run the service had increased to £2,000 per day.

1995

- Springhill Hospice passed the sixth year milestone. Admissions October 1989 – October 1995 totalled 1,730, discharges 890, deaths in Hospice 831.

- Dr Louise Foreman joined as full-time Consultant Practitioner in Palliative Medicine.

- Most patients were being visited in their homes before admission.

- November 1995 the link corridor was built between main Hospice and the Springhill Suite.

- Hospice was working towards Investors in People.

- We advertised for a second Medical Officer.

- For the first year income exceeded £1,000,000 (75% raised in Rochdale).

- The start of the National Lottery seemed to cause a substantial reduction in donations – this was recovered.

- 8th December – Santa special train from Bury to Rawtenstall and back.

- Ken Davies joined as fund-raiser/PR.

- Daily cost of running the Hospice was £2,250.

- A special event took place in October, a display of craft work done by patients and their families and friends.

1996

- February – the Hospice went 'live' with the recording of patient records on computer, the system is called Palcare.

- Rochdale TEC/Business Link commissioned the artist Peter Sunderland (a long standing friend of the Hospice) to produce a painting of the building.

- Admissions to the patients' unit increased as the Hospice was now providing some acute treatments previously available only in hospitals.

- The Out-Patient Clinic began at one morning per week. This provided assessment and treatment for patients not otherwise treated at the Hospice.

- 1996 saw an increase in the lettings of the Springhill Suite.

- 1st auction of Bygones was held.

- In June the Founder Matron retired after establishing the foundation of the nursing care provided by the Hospice.

- Mrs Christine Webb was appointed as Chief Executive and joined in June.

- During 1996 Dr Louise Forman became a regular contributor to the Cardiff Palliative Care Diploma for Doctors and also became an examiner on the course.

- Dorothy Swire jointed the Hospice in June 1996 as Income Services Manager.

- Daily cost of running the Hospice increased to £2,400.

- The second-hand furniture shop opened in Oldham Road.

- November – another new service was launched – the Crisis Intervention Service.

1997

- 1st July the Duchess of Norfolk, CBE, founder and chairman of Help the Hospices formally opened the Springhill Suite. Emma Duffy, niece of Kay Scott founder Matron, presented a bouquet to the Duchess.

- The Duchess of Norfolk accepted an invitation to become a Patron of the Hospice.

- Springhill gained Investors in People – not easy but a worthwhile exercise (First Hospice in the UK to do so).

- Appointment of a part-time Chaplin the Rev Kevin Dunn.

- October – Day Hospice extended to operate four days each week (Monday – Thursday inclusive).

- Tommy of 'Tommy's shop' died. He was the father of first Matron Kay Scott.

- New event held – The Wit of the Year.

- 4th Charity Shop opened in November in Littleborough.

- 2nd Auction of Bygones held – raising £3,000.

- In 1997 it cost over £2,500 per day to Keep the Hospice open.

- Late 1997 the Hospice Lottery was set up. First winner was Mrs Barbara Peace. Her cheque was presented by the comedian Jimmy Cricket at the Wheatsheaf Shopping Centre, Rochdale.

- Springhill was awarded the Rochdale Civic Society Award.

1998

- Start of 10th year, during the first nine years the Hospice welcomed over 3,000 patients.

- Work of Hospice Doctors extended to include palliative care in a number of settings, the Hospice, Nursing Homes and in patients' own home.

- Liaison with The Christies Hospital and Springhill was now taking care of patients earlier in their illness e.g. taking people directly from Christies and caring for them after chemotherapy and radiotherapy.

- Figures for last 12 months showed at least two thirds of patients were discharged.

- Recruited 17 new volunteers, 65% were under 20 years of age.

- At end of November 1998 all the shops including Tommy's had increased their income and represented (between them) 25% of all of Hospice income.

- Dame Mary Peters visited the Hospice.

- Daily cost of running the Hospice reached £2,900.

1999

- Start of year 10th celebration – Princess Alexander visited Springhill and received a bouquet from Abigail Webb (daughter of the CEO).

- Golden Tree of Life was erected on an internal wall. Individual leaves were to be used to celebrate individuals' contributions to the Hospice.

- Garden Party took place as part of the 10th year celebration.

- By the end of 1999 over 3,000 patients and their families had benefited from the very special care we provide.

- NHS was providing 25% of necessary funding, remainder came from generosity of people of Rochdale.

- Being assessed by outside bodies having to adhere to very high standards in every aspect of Hospice life – clinical priorities, food hygiene, health and safety are regularly checked.

- Treated more patients than ever before, 338 in-patients. Day hospice catered for some 3,000 attendances.

- Springhill 90, Castleton and Whitworth support groups were still in existence.

- Charity Abseil Day from Rochdale Town Hall Clock Tower as part of Charity Abseil Day. Organized by Rochdale Round Table. Lorna Fitzsimmons, then member of Parliament from Rochdale took part.

- The Hospice Lottery game celebrated its one hundredth draw in September 1999.

- Daily cost of running the Hospice was £3,164.

- Team of 54 paid staff and 350 volunteers (treated in exactly the same way as those on the payroll).

- With a workforce of over 400 personnel the Hospice was one of the biggest employers in the whole Rochdale Metropolitan area.

- Annual turnover of £1.25M.

- Yearly target of £800,000 for fund-raising.

- A short history of the first ten years was written by Norman Frisby, Trustee and published at the end of 1999 its title 'A World of Good' was taken from a quotation by a patient.

2000

- Launch of Hospice Capital Renewal Appeal 2000/2002. This was another challenge – to raise £205,000 to purchase new essential equipment.

- Applied to the National Lottery Board for funding to build a small Education Unit next to Day Hospice (lecture room, library, IT room and 2 offices).

- December we received a grant of £275,462 to build the Education Unit.
- By November 2000 the Community Palliative Care Support Team was in place.
- During 2002 the cost of providing Hospice Care was over £1.2M.
- Volunteers worked 25,584 hours, at minimum wage that equated to £92,102.
- The number of young people wanting to do voluntary work (towards their Duke of Edinburgh Award) increased.
- Springhill hosted the first ever day conference of Hospice Chaplains in the Diocese of Manchester.
- Andrew Nutter devised and cooked the meal (along with the Town Hall staff) for the 8th Annual Woman of Rochdale luncheon. Woman of the year was the 100 years young Gladys Emerson.
- Early in 2000 a volunteer, Louis Blank was granted a Millennium award for production of a magazine for staff and volunteers. Part of this enabled the Hospice to buy a computer, scanner, printer and digital camera. The latter was used for photographing events and to enable patients to see photos more quickly.
- The Hospice computer network was re-cabled to enable the Hospice to keep up with rapid advances in technology. This means that the Hospice could keep up with legislative demands and the demands of purchasers to present info in their required formats.
- By the end of 2000 – the Hospice had five shops, one donated stock centre and Tommy's shop in the Hospice building.
- Staff got together to look at ways of supporting the children who have contact with the Hospice. BBC's Children in Need gave a grant to help with staff training and money for equipment.
- Three children's days were held where bereaved children joined in activities designed to help realise they are not alone.
- Lynn Hutton joined as Education Manager.
- Induction package was produced for volunteers.
- Daily cost of Hospice rose to £3,430.
- In June Help the Hospices told us that BAE Systems Charity Challenge teams across the country had nominated the Hospice movement as their chosen charity.

- November a new shop opened at 543 Market Street, Rochdale.

2001

- The Education Unit, funded by National Lottery Community Fund was completed in August.

- In-patient area upgraded with piped oxygen, better bathing facilities, and a conservatory donated and built for use by patients and their families.

- Terry McNicholas of Sunset Windows donated (FOC) the conservatory.

- Ken Davis (fund-raising director) decided to 'semi-retire' and Ian Jenkins was appointed as Fund-raising Manager.

- Dame Mary Peters was speaker at Women of Rochdale Luncheon – she then went on to become a Patron of Springhill Hospice.

- The Nursing team expanded with the appointment of two specialist Palliative Care nurses who work both in the Hospice and in the community.

- The first junior Doctor in training at the Hospice – secondment .

- NHS, Social Services and the voluntary sector came together to start a new Community Palliative Care Scheme (Compass) which allowed carers to go into patients homes to provide help. (This scheme no longer operates).

- The people of Rochdale donated in excess of the enormous sum of £205,000 (in nine months) required to update the Hospice building and facilities.

- Mayor of Rochdale, Councillor Irene Davidson chose Springhill Hospice as her mayoral charity for 2001/2 (third time a mayor elected to sponsor the Hospice).

- Two conferences held in May 'The way forward in Palliative Care', October's conference was concerned with religious and cultural awareness in Palliative Care, with facilitators from Christian, Hindu, Jewish, Muslim and Sikh religions.

- Daily cost of running the Hospice went up 6% on last year to £3,660.

2002

- BAE Systems Charity Challenge Team from Chadderton received a national award in recognition of raising £75,000 for the three Hospices they chose to sponsor.

- Dr Fiona Cooper joined the Hospice as clinical assistant and subsequently as Hospice Doctor (she had been a visiting Dr) to replace Dr Phillip Lomax who left to become Consultant and Medical Director at St Ann's Hospice.

- Since late 1989 almost 5,000 people had benefited from the Hospice's hospitality/services.

- Mayor of Rochdale Councillor Irene Davidson raised almost £8,500 for the Hospice (providing state of the art beds).

- Chaplain Rev Kevin Dunn, together with Dr Forman completed a research paper on 'Facing death with Confidence'. This was published in the European Journal of Palliative Care.

- Two art auctions helped raised just over £4,600 – Sir Cyril Smith was the celebrity auctioneer at one.

- At the Charity Finance award ceremony Springhill Hospice won two awards. We received the award for the highest profitability for charities with fewer than 20 shops. We also came 43rd out of 106, including national organizations, in donated stock sales.

- Oldham Road Shop celebrated the fact that since opening 10 years ago it had turned over £1M of business.

- Two Conferences, in May on Rehabilitation in Palliative Care. The October Conference was on Quality of Life Issues.

- 16 fund-raising events held throughout the year (12 is the norm).

- In May Councillor Lil Murphy chose Springhill as one of her two mayoral charities.

- Daily running costs now stood at £4,060 per day.

2003

- 20th Anniversary of the appeal 'A Hospice for Rochdale'.

- Close to 6,000 patients and families had been cared for since the Hospice opened.

- A full review of Day Hospice provision was planned/carried out.

- A quarterly remembrance service was held.

- Embracing new challenges in palliative medicine, the Hospice was now able to admit patients with more complex needs.

- More patients attended Day Hospice for procedures which used to need a visit to a hospital.

- Legislative requirements during the year brought major changes to Hospice policies, procedures and documentation.

- Week commencing 14th June was National Hospice Awareness Week.

- Pressure from local Primary Care Trusts required us to provide a wealth of information in order to secure the small NHS portion of our funding.

- Mrs Peggy Nutter from the Oldham Road Charity Shop was awarded the MBE for the valued work she does for Springhill and St Mary's Balderstone.

- Councillor Lil Murphy handed over nearly £9,000 raised during her mayoral term.

- Councillor Sultan Ali chose the Hospice as one of his charities for his mayoral year.

- Being chosen as one of the Mayor of Rochdale's charities for three years running was invaluable, not only in financial terms but also in Public Relations.

- Daily cost of running the Hospice was now £4,424.

2004

- A Big Lottery Grant enabled us to work in conjunction with the PCTs on the planning of a 24 hr Advice Line which would be launched in January 2005.

- The 15th Anniversary refurbishment appeal was launched to upgrade much of the in-patient area and to build an extension to increase the overnight accommodation facilities available for families.

- The 'Building on Friendship' initiative was launched. Supporters were able to buy a plaque on the 'Friendship wall' which went on to become a permanent feature of the Hospice.

- The average daily cost went up 1.5%. to £4,490.

- All nursing staff underwent an intensive training programme to enable them to operate the planned 24 hr advice line effectively.

- A newly reformed Bereavement Group met monthly at the Hospice (and continued to do so in 2009).

- We were faced with the need to begin to implement the integrated care pathway aimed at standardizing care and good symptom control for all patients at the end of their lives, whether they die at home, in a Hospital or in a Hospice.

- This year we continued to monitor timescales. Average time from initial referral to being offered a bed is 1.4 days. The time from being offered a bed to coming into the Hospice averages 1 day.

- A lot of time was spent obtaining grants to help meet the £700,000 needed for the planned refurbishment.

- We secured £15,000 from the Co-operative charitable Foundation, £15,000 from the Foyle Foundation and £3,000 from Township Funds.

- Volunteers worked 675 hours per week saving the Hospice £160,000 per year.

- At Volunteers' Christmas party 13 volunteers received a 15 years award – all having been here since 2nd October 1989.

- Peggy Nutter, MBE died in May. A plaque was put in 'Peggy's shop' in recognition of the work she had done at 445 Oldham Road over so many years.

- Since the first draw of Springhill Hospice in 1997 – the lottery had generated almost £500,000.

- Hospice Care Assistant Cora Magerison-Williams set off from Florida in February to cycle across the USA. She finished three months later in Los Angeles and raised thousands of pounds for the Hospice.

- In March Hospice Patrons Meg Johnson and Charles Foster helped launch the Tesco 'Time to Care' appeal which enabled Tesco staff at stores in Middleton, Alkrington, Bamford and Rochdale to raise funds for us throughout the year.

- June was national Hospice Awareness month therefore, very busy with party events.

- In the summer a gala day was held at the Hospice, two successful car boot sales were held in August and September.

2005/6

- We received £48k from the People's Millions (Part of the National Lottery). We secured the grant after a public vote on national TV. This was for work on the grounds at the front of the Hospice.

- In February Nick Dent (our gardener) with this grant, completed a project with the help of local school children and Skill Force. Together they redesigned the car park making it safer. They also developed a lovely garden area. Coverage on Granada Reports was lovely for the children and showed off our wonderful Hospice across the North West.

- In June an extension was completed. This provided additional single rooms for patients and overnight accommodation for families.

- Springhill Crafts Support group funded the soft furnishings of the new patient bedrooms.

- 24 hour advice line was launched 31st January 2005 with three years funding from the Big Lottery Fund.

- In Sept 2005 Rev Martin McGonigle joined as Chaplain with a brief to lead on pastoral and spiritual care for all groups concerned at the Hospice.

- Relationships with external organizations continued to thrive – including much continued support from Zen Internet who as a Rochdale company are on record in expressing their pleasure to take any opportunity to help a leading local charity. Among other things they donated a computer for the patient lounge.

- The Catering team won 'Gold' in the healthy foods award. This award is presented by the Environmental Health Dept to organizations demonstrating a very high standard in nutrition, hygiene and staff training.

- We continued to apply for funding wherever possible. Main tasks for 2007 were identified as refurbishing four single rooms to the same very high standard as the rooms in the extension and to improving showering facilities in the in-patient unit.

- The efforts of our marvellous volunteers were now saving the Hospice more than £419,000 per year.

- In May 2006 there was a recruitment campaign for volunteers. This resulted in 30 new volunteers, of these 11 were aged 16 – 20. This encouraged the Hospice to present the first young volunteer of year award. The winner was 17 year old Amaranti Marti who had worked at the Hospice for 13 months.

- A 20 year service badge was introduced for volunteers.

- Average daily running cost was now £5,000 breaking down to £208 per hour, £3.47 per minute, or £312 per bed per day.

- The 11th annual Auction of Bygones raised £7,002.

- Peggy's shop on Oldham Road was refurbished and reopened by the Mayor, Councillor Ashley Dearnley and Mayoress, Councillor Beryl Wright.

- The Mayoral appeal by Councillor Ashley Dearnley who chose the Hospice as his charity. His aim was to raise £20,000 for an Arjo bath. In the end he raised £37,000 which not only bought the bath but also paid for all fixtures and fittings for the whole bathroom.

- At the beginning of November Mrs Dorothy Lee was declared champion sunflower grower for the tallest sunflower. She then celebrated her 94th birthday. Her week ended by winning first prize in the Hospice Lottery!

2007

- February 2007 Gladys Liddell, shop volunteer celebrated her 90th birthday.

- Everyone looking forward to the big refurbishment programme which began in October 2007. The four original single rooms, toilet areas and shower rooms to be refurbished to a high standard. Made possible by successful grant application to the Department of Health.

- Advanced nursed practitioner Staff Nurse Nazma Salam was recruited on to the programme and began a 12 month programme of learning. The programme was to be substantiated by accreditation at Masters level at Salford University.

- Lymphodema key worker training programme Staff Nurse Donna Chapman was seconded into this in June 2007 – no lymphodema practitioner in Heywood/Middleton/Rochdale Area, therefore sufferers had to travel.

- Springhill committed to providing a lymphodema service for the local population from 2008.

- Six month pilot programme of the 24 hour advice line – for Oldham was started in July 2007.

- New diversional therapist role created – providing art and craft therapies, games, quizzes and other activities for those patients who want to participate. This enables the nurses to maintain the 'nursing' role.

- Over last year – increasing number of patients with a non-cancer diagnosis were referred to Hospice services. This reflects the fact than non-cancer patients also require palliative care and Hospice services.

- The Hospice website designed by Zen Internet went live in Jan 2007.

- In May we heard that Dept of Health had awarded us a grant of £423,224 for capital refurbishment – work was completed, as planned, mid way through 2008.

- In October Nick Dent our gardener was recognised when the Hospice won the Best Hospital Grounds category of the North West in Bloom Awards (part of Britain in Bloom Competition) organized by the Royal Horticultural Society.

- In July Hospice held its first ever 'Pamper Day' when 26 carers came for a day of pampering. Welcomed with bucks fizz breakfast.

- Volunteer Awards:

  - 25 volunteers – 2 yr medal   - 9 volunteers – 15 yr medal

  - 8 volunteers – 5 yr medal   - 2 volunteers – 20 yr medal

  - 18 volunteers – 10 yr medal

- 2006/7 - £118,194 raised by in-house activities, £9,193 through support groups and £80,733 – third part/joint events – a total of £208,120.

- Winter 2006 – first ever Santa Run.

- Inaugural Ladies' Midnight Walk.

- Hospice Patron Dame Mary Peters hosted another fund-raising dinner.

- PGC Demolition held their first 'Hard Hats for Charity' dinner and raised £35,000 for the Hospice.

- The Shamrocks Tug of War Team bought the Hospice a new estate car.

- In November 2007 Springhill Crafts Support Group, founded in 2004, celebrated raising £50,000 for specific 'projects'.

- Death of fund-raiser Annie Wilson in July 2007 – she had only joined the Hospice in November of 2006.

- Dean Connaughton joined as Community Fund-raiser.

- 2006/7 Gross income from shops exceeded £400,000 – up 6% on previous year.

- All Hospice shops were now refurbished.

- Purchased own transit van – which enables faster response to requests for collection.

- For the first time we took a stall on Rochdale market to sell excess bric a brac – very successful in terms of both profit and awareness raising.

- Profit for first nine months of registration with the Greater Manchester Waste Development Agency was £3,888.

- Arrangements with Recycle Solutions/Rochdale MBC for recycling textile banks brought in £4,350 in 12 months.

- November 2007 Littleborough shop celebrated its 10th Anniversary – party held for past and present volunteers – shop had raised £800,000 in that time.

2008

- When Princess Ann opened the Hospice in 1989 it was very much on a wing and a prayer. Now eagerly expecting the 20 Anniversary.

- £423,225 from Dept of Health funded major building programme – newly refurbished – new reception and shop area – new lightening throughout Hospice, additional room for Day Hospice, quiet place and used for craft work.

- When builders were in we decided to have kitchen refitted – received a grant of £70,000 from the Wolfson Foundation to cover this.

- Margaret Geoghegan, Chairman of Board of Trustees received the wonderful honour of the freedom of Borough of Rochdale in 2008 – ceremony 22nd February 2009.

- 24 hour Advice Line continued and was extended to cover the Oldham Borough.

- April 2008 the Hospice officially opened the lymphodema clinic, initially to run one day per week. We have successfully acquired funding to continue this service through the commissioning channels of the HMRPCT.

- A further application to Help the Hospices was successful and £32,800 was awarded to us towards the cost of providing a carer's advisor.

- Jim Cunningham joined as Education Co-ordinator.

- Electronic link to the Path Lab at the Royal Oldham Lab went live – enabling far faster access of results, with clear benefits for our patients.

- Created an in-house laundry service (previously we paid to have this done at the Hospital) now have three washing machines and three driers. In 2009 will look at feasibility of increasing the laundry space to continue with the cost savings of doing our own.

- Snack menu service now operating all day.

- Following a review of in-patient services we recruited into the new role of Discharge Co-ordinator.

- Our volunteers saved the Hospice more than £395,000 this year.

- Gross income from shops was £424,449, up £7,000 from previous year.

- Daisy Kirk from the Littlebrough shop celebrated her 90th birthday.

- When the charity stall at Rochdale market is available we took it to maintain income – our retail stewards operate the stall.

- The Rochdale Observer created the 'Can you spare a minute' Appeal. (It takes £5 to keep Hospice open for a minute). By the end 2008 the appeal raised over £30,000. The appeal mascot – Robbie the bear has become a very popular character.

- One Robbie was photographed with Robinho the Manchester City footballer. Robinho signed some of the photos for us. Robbie also went travelling with Dame Mary Peters, our Patron and had his adventures reported in the Observer.

- Andrew Nutter held Nutters Crystal Ball to celebrate the restaurant's 15th Anniversary – attended by a number of celebrity chefs – it raised £7,500 towards the Rochdale Observer's Appeal.

- People participating in the Great Manchester Run raised nearly £5,000.

- PGC Demolition's 2nd Hard hats for Charity Dinner in October 2008 raised a staggering £36,000 for us.

- The 20th anniversary celebrations started with a wonderful evening in the company of Dame Mary Peters at Rochdale Town Hall.

   (We plan a spectacular Grand 20th Anniversary Masquerade Ball on 17th October 2009).

- It now cost over £2.5m per year to provide all our services to patients and their families.

- Rochdale Observer set up its 'Spare a Minute' campaign to raise funds for the Hospice.

- Visit of Lord Lieutenant of Greater Manchester, Mr Warren J Smith to Springhill.

- Daily cost has now risen to £6,000.

- Councillor Robin Parker chose Springhill as one of his two Mayoral charities.

2009

- 22nd February – Ceremony at Rochdale Town Hall conferring the Freedom of the Borough on Margaret Geoghegan MBE.

- February – Mrs Geoghegan, Mrs Webb and several trustees represented the Hospice at the Evensong Service at Manchester Cathedral for Mr Warren J Smith, Lord Lieutenant of Greater Manchester.

- March 2009 – Margaret Geoghegan and Christine Webb were presented to Her Majesty the Queen and HRH Prince Phillip at St James Palace as part of the 25th Anniversary of Help the Hospices.

- Working group of Trustees and staff set up to look at Hospice strategy for the period 2009 – 2014.

- Dr Chris Pick successfully completed his Diploma in Palliative Medicine.

- Masked Ball held at Rochdale Town Hall to celebrate the 20th anniversary.

- Publication of the 20th Anniversary Book.

Daily Costs of Running the Hospice

1990	£630
1991	£1,325
1992	£1,461
1993	£1,750
1994	£2,000
1995	£2,250
1996	£2,400
1997	£2,500
1998	£2,900
1999	£3,164 This was the first year when our running costs passed £1M per year
2000	£3,430
2001	£3,660
2002	£4,060
2003	£4,424
2004	£4,490
2005/6	£5,000 (£208 per hour, £312 per bed per day)
2006	£5,233
2007	£5,615 – It now costs £2m per year to provide all our services to patients and their families
2008	£6,000
2009	£6,500

CONTACT US

Springhill Hospice
Broad Lane
Rochdale OL16 4PZ
Tel: 01706 649920
Fax: 01706 644943

Email: enquiries@springhillhospice.nhs.uk

Admissions:
Sr Christine Fostinis, Admissions Co-ordinator
Email: Christine.Fostinis@ springhillhospice.nhs.uk

Fund-raising:
Ian Jenkins Fund-raising Manager
Email: Ian.Jenkins@ springhillhospice.nhs.uk

24 Hour Advice Line
Sr Claire Brown, Specialist Palliative Care Nurse
Tel: 01706 653555
Email: Claire.Brown@ springhillhospice.nhs.uk

Springhill Hospice Charity Shops
Information Centre and Furniture Shop
425 Oldham Road
Rochdale OL16 4SZ
Tel: 01706 638231
Fax: 01706 861762

Email: springhill.shops@zen.co.uk

Springhill Hospice Charity Shops
445:Oldham Road, Rochdale
Tel: 01706 869406

136 Yorkshire Street Rochdale
Tel: 01706 347035

22 Harehill Road Littleborough
Tel: 01706 375268

543 Market Street, Whitworth
Tel: 01706 854563.

To Volunteer at the Hospice
Tel: 01706 649920

To Volunteer at the Hospice Shops
Tel: 01706 638231

To find out about leaving a Legacy
Tel: 01706 649920
Email: fundraising@springhillhospice.nhs.uk

To Discuss an Admission
Tel: 01706 649920 **The Admissions Co-ordinator**

To Discuss Collection of Goods
Tel: 01706 638231

Mayor Jean Hornby, Mrs Geoghegan and Jack Price, Deputy Grand Superintendent of Rochdale District Provincial Grand Lodge of East Lancashire at the opening of the sensory garden on Saturday 5th May 2007.

Part of the last major extension in 2007/8.

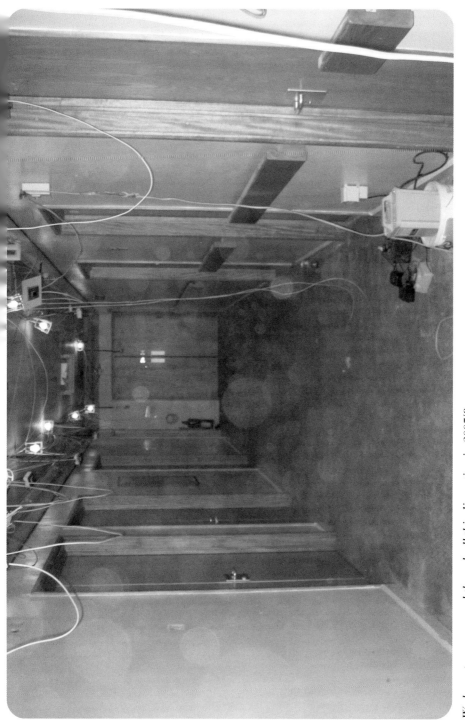

Work went on as normal through all this disruption in 2007/8.

16. 2007, Hospice Patron Dame Mary Peters LL with Tania from Retail Services.

17. 2008, the refurbished reception area and Tommy's Shop at Broad Lane.

18. 2008, Elaine Ferguson in the Hospice's remodeled kitchen.

19. The three new single rooms added in the 2007/8 refurbishment.

20. *The People's Millions Garden created by Nick Dent, Skill Force and a group of local young people.*

21. *Pat Harding, Day Hospice Sister (left) and Volunteer Margaret MacDonald with a Day Patient. (Photograph courtesy of Rochdale Observer).*

22. *Robby, the Rochdale Observer 'Can you spare a minute' appeal bear with Robinho of Manchester City Football Club. (Photograph courtesy of MCFC).*

23. *The present - the Main Entrance at Broad Lane.*

24. *Maureen Styles and Christine Jones with the Springhill Crafts Support Group which includes many Hospice Volunteers. (Photograph courtesy of Rochdale Observer).*

25. *Day Hospice nurses Carole O'Brian, Lynne McOwen and Debbie Johnson. (Photograph courtesy of Rochdale Observer).*

26. *Lymphodema Nurse, Donna Chapman and specialist Palliative Nurse Nasma Salam Ahmad. (Photograph courtesy of Rochdale Observer).*

27. *2009 Diversional Therapist, Anwen Maitland with a Memory Box made by a Day Hospice Patient. (Photograph courtesy of Rochdale Observer).*

Preachi_ ◡

at Funerals

by

Ian Bunting

Director of Ordinands, Diocese of Southwe

GROVE BOOKS LIMITED
Bramcote   Nottingham   NG9 3 DS

CONTENTS

ACKNOWLEDGMENTS

I gladly acknowledge the help of Robert Crossley, Robin Leaver, Trevor Lloyd and Michael Vasey in amending the original draft, and the willingness of Pat Walker to type the script. The illustration on the front cover was drawn by Peter Ashton.

NOTE RE THIRD EDITION

In the third edition, I have taken the opportunity to update some of the information given in the text. I have been surprised at how sensitive I have become, in just a few years, to the need for inclusive language. Although I am aware that twelve years ago, when the booklet was first published, it was only an issue with a few, today it could appear that this booklet is written for clergymen, male ordinands and male readers. Far from it. In fact, I have learned much about preaching at funerals from a succession of sensitive women colleagues at Chester-le-Street, in particular Isabel Wells, Rosemary Nixon, Margaret Bianchi, Amiel Osmaston, and Alison White. Although I have not changed the language, I hope they will accept this edition as a warm tribute to them. Some of them had to face the hurt of meeting suspicion, and even rejection, from bereaved families who felt that it was only a proper funeral it if was conducted by a man. I would like this edition to be a way of saying thank you to these friends and colleagues.

First Edition November 1978

Second Edition April 1981

Third Edition (by Grove Books Limited) February 1990

ISSN 0305-3067

ISBN 1 85174 136 4

INTRODUCTION

No occasion offers a greater challenge to the sensitive pastoral preacher than the funeral service. Whether he knows the family of the deceased or not, he cannot hope to fathom the deep personal feelings with which they come to church. He is moreover president at a service which confronts him with questions about his own calling. Is he there as a folk priest to help the bereaved through this ancient rite of passage, or is he an apostle with good news to bring of God's eternal purpose for men and women? Most ministers will see themselves as both. They proclaim the hope of resurrection in Christ but they cannot do it in total disregard for the context in which they speak.

In 1944, towards the end of his life, Dietrich Bonhoeffer looked forward to a period of what he called, *Aristocratic Christianity*.[1] This booklet makes a plea for just such a stance over against man's last enemy. Helpful themes for the pastoral preacher include a call to repentance in the face of coming judgment, a recollection of the life and witness of those who die in faith and the joyful expectation of glory to come in the resurrection of the living and the dead. Long ago Martin Bucer, the reformer from Strasbourg, in commenting on the 1549 Book of Common Prayer offered this agenda.

'. . . ,to warn ourselves of the terrible nature of the sins by which men bring sickness and death on themselves, and to press upon ourselves the need for sincere and constant penitence. Also if it is appropriate, when the church has suffered a particular loss in the passing of a dead brother, to explain it diligently to those present. Next from the promises and resurrection of the Lord to confirm ourselves in the faith of the resurrection and to comfort ourselves for the departure of a devout brother: and if he gave a shining example of new life, to recount it for the glory of God and the imitation of ourselves who are left. Finally to encourage ourselves to continual and effective meditation upon the future life, and to make suitable and wholesome preparation to cross with joyful minds from this lost world to the Lord Christ.'[2]

The purpose of the present booklet is to help the pastoral preacher to come to terms with his role and to prepare his message and also to suggest some resources.

---

[1] Eberhard Bethge, *Dietrich Bonhoeffer* (Collins, London, 1970) p.768.
[2] E. C. Whitaker, *Martin Bucer and the Book of Common Prayer* (Alcuin Club/Mayhew-McCrimmon, Great Wakering, 1974) p.127f.

3

1. THE ROLE OF THE PREACHER

None of the occasional services depends more upon the minister than the funeral. In spite of the attempt of modern rites to encourage greater participation, the fact is that most congregations depend heavily upon the leadership of the minister. Even if they are familiar with the shape of the funeral service, the setting is strange and the focus of the eye, when not upon the coffin or the mourners, is upon the minister at the front. The strong biblical imagery of the set service sounds odd in the ears of irregular worshippers. Everything conspires to put the burden upon the one who leads the service.

(i) The Minister is Master of Ceremonies

The minister plans, organizes and controls the service. First he will need to gain information about the deceased and his family. Undertakers normally give the necessary details about the deceased's age, occupation, last illness, surviving relatives and, most important, who will be present at the service, although a home visit before the funeral will give access to a fuller profile. It is, for instance, vital to get the correct and familiar name. The use of the name, in the service, dropped out in the 1552 Prayer Book. In the ASB 1980 services it happily returns to add that important personal touch which recognizes the deceased as an individual, a unique creation of God.

Secondly, the minister is responsible for selecting and planning the service. Canon B3.4 states that persons concerned may object beforehand to the service selected by the minister. The initiative lies with the minister but he needs to consult the family. When it comes to rites of passage, ASB 1980 is conservative in character but the family may prefer the Prayer Book Service, with which they are familiar, to the new service which for them is strange and jarring with its new Lord's Prayer and participation in modern prayers. The rhythm of the traditional office supports the mourners through the strain of the funeral. Is it right for the minister, at this sensitive moment, to disturb them either in the choice of service or in what he says in the sermon? To this question we shall have to return below.

Thirdly, the conduct of a funeral service calls upon all the minister's skills of leadership. Normally no choir leads the singing and sometimes there is no music. Choirs and hymns tend to draw a congregation together. Without them the minister in a few short minutes has the task of bringing together people who come from all quarters into a united act of worship. The minister helps the congregation to that unity if he has a calm confident voice, if he gives clear directions and if he himself concentrates on the service; which is easier said than done if it happens to be the fourth funeral he has conducted that day. The minister also gives non-verbal leadership by his dignified movement and the ability to look people in the eye. In these ways he not only controls the service and provides the right context, in which he will preach a word from God, but also gives a firm stable point of Christian confidence in a situation where worshippers come together with all sorts of disparate motives.

4

(ii) The Minister is an expressive leader of the congregation

A healthy fear of saying too much about the deceased at the funeral has persisted since the Reformation. The puritans were critical of the practice of putting burial sermons in the place of requiem masses. They argued that such sermons encouraged the idea that the dead benefit from them, also that the minister often had to preach a sermon with insufficient time to prepare and to study the Scriptures. They further objected that sermons, preached at the funerals of the wealthy and powerful and not the poor, betrayed a sinful and false respect of persons. The Prayer Book Office makes no provision for a sermon. In ASB 1980 it is now an option. Richard Hooker in the 16th century defended the inclusion of a burial sermon and thought it in no way inappropriate to make reference to the deceased.

> 'The life and the death of Saints is precious in God's sight. Let it not seem odious in our eyes if both the one and the other be spoken of then especially when the present occasion doth make men's minds the more capable of such speech. The care no doubt of the living both to live and to die well must needs be somewhat increased, when they know that their departure shall not be folded up in silence but the ears of many be made acquainted with it. Moreover, when they hear how mercifully God hath dealt with their brethren in their last need, besides the praise which they give to God and the joy which they have or should have by reason of their fellowship and communion with saints, is not their hope not also much confirmed against the day of their own dissolution?'[1]

Hooker is saying that people are ready to learn from the faith and example of the dead. He sees the concentration of the mourners upon the person of the departed not as a hindrance to the preaching of the gospel but rather as an opportunity.

David Sheppard has described the expressive leader as 'the man who can put into words the strong feelings of the group . . .'.[2] At a funeral the congregation comes with strong feelings which look for expression in a Christian service which, as we shall see, is founded upon hope of resurrection in Christ. The mourners feel despair, resentment, guilt and resignation but the Christian minister has no brief to major on those themes. He may, however, draw together many of the emotions represented in the worshippers if he strikes a chord of thanksgiving for the dead. Such a note redirects those who are pre-occupied with their sense of loss. For one thing it acknowledges and accepts that sense of bereavement as something that is wholesome. It is an entirely proper response on the part of everyone present.

> 'No man is an Island entire of itself. Every man is a piece of the continent, a part of the main; if a clod be washed away by the sea, Europe is the less, as well as if a promontory were, as well as if a manor of thy friends or of thine own were; any man's death diminishes me, because I am involved in mankind; and therefore never send to know for whom the bell tolls. It tolls for thee'.[3]

1 Richard Hooker, *Of the Laws of Ecclesiastical Polity*, Book 5 (J. M. Dent, London, 1907) p.403.
2 David Sheppard, *Built as a City* (Hodder and Stoughton, London 1974) p.287.
3 John Donne, ed. John Hayward, *Complete Poetry and Selected Prose*, (Nonesuch Press, London, 1929) p.538.

The note of thanksgiving in the funeral service seizes upon this sense of loss and turns it to God's praise. We are lent to each other and we receive each other by grace. Every person is a gift from God to us, a gift not to be possessed, for that would make us guilty of idolatry, but a gift nonetheless to be enjoyed. Such a view of other people transforms our relationships with them when they are alive and brings the response of gratitude for them when they die. Even the most tragic death in the most unpleasant circumstances cannot deny us the possibility of saying thank you to God for something. If it is a young mother killed in a road accident, her grief-stricken husband and children can say thank you for all that she meant to them. If it is a drug-addict who has killed himself with an overdose, then maybe there are those at the funeral who can remember how he used to laugh as a child or others, themsleves addicts, who valued his friendliness or even his pathetic dependence upon them. If it is a pauper's funeral from the mental hospital and only a hospital representative and the undertaker are present, then here too is one of God's created beings. Shall we praise the grace of a creator-God less in this man than in another? In many heart-rending bereavements we say, 'there but for the grace of God go I!' and the note of thanksgiving is not for the departed but for ourselves. There is, nevertheless, as John Donne recognized, a deeper bond between the world and myself; not only does a death diminish me but every life enhances mine.

The expressive leader of the congregation also draws out, where it is true and appropriate, the lessons to be learnt from the faith and life of the departed. The limit of our knowledge of any other person renders this a dangerous undertaking. The puritans of the 17th century, in their objection to the Book of Common Prayer, used to criticize the assured language of the Burial Office.[1] The bishops in their reply stated:

> 'We see not why these words may not be said of any person whom we dare not say is damned, and it were a breach of charity to say so even of those whose repentance we do not see: for whether they do not inwardly and heartily repent, even at the last act, who knows? and that God will not even then pardon them upon such repentance, who dares say? It is better to be charitable, and hope the best, than rashly to condemn'[2].

The ASB 1980 services make no confident assertions about the past faith or future destiny of the deceased. To this extent the uneasiness of the puritans has eventually prevailed. The opportunity does present itself, however, in the sermon to speak of the departed and there is long precedent in the Church of England for doing so.

[1] 'Foreasmuch as it hath pleased Almighty God of his great mercy to take unto himself the soul of our dear brother here departed: we therefore commit his body to the ground in sure and certain hope of resurrection to eternal life.' (In the 1662 Book of Common Prayer the preposition 'the' was added to 'resurrection' in the committal and thus made the reference to the future state of the departed less particular). We may note also 'that when we depart this life, we may rest in him, as our hope is this our brother doth.' and 'that we with this our brother, and all other departed in the true faith of thy holy name, may have our perfect confirmation and bliss.'

[2] Edward Cardwell, *A History of Conferences And Other Proceedings connected with the Revision of the Book of Common Prayer from 1552 to 1690* (Oxford University Press, 1841) p.361f.

Almost all Christians look back to the life and witness of Christians now dead who once, when alive, deeply influenced the course of their earthly pilgrimage. In some cases we owe our faith itself, humanly speaking, to some old saint who spoke to us of Jesus Christ in such a way that the Master stepped out of the pages of a neglected Bible to encounter us at a critical point in our lives. We naturally want to model ourselves upon his example and commitment. Paul was happy to call people to imitate him and we are making the same kind of appeal when we speak of the dead in such a way that our people remember their example and follow their practice (1 Cor. 4.15-17, Phil. 4.9, 2 Thess. 3.9). We are reinforcing their own feelings about the deceased and underlining the lessons for the whole church.[1]

(iii) The Minister is a Messenger of Jesus Christ

The preacher may strike three gospel chords; the certainty and seriousness of death and judgment, the hope of resurrection, and the ultimate unity of all believers in Christ.

(a) *The Certainty and Seriousness of Death.* Modern Christendom gives insufficient recognition to the certainty and seriousness of death. There are several reasons for this. Twentieth century man has distanced himself from sickness and death. Comparatively few people die at home. Fewer people care to view the corpse. We use a host of euphemisms to disguise the reality of the event. We protect children and young people. The undertaker sees to the details. People prefer a quiet short service. We feel that it is not proper to show our grief in public. Many cemetery chapels and crematoria positively encourage this mood of detachment. In Forest Lawn Cemetery in California the 'Builder's Creed', recorded in marble and dated New Year's Day 1917, begins, 'I believe in a happy Eternal Life. I believe those of us who are left behind should be glad in the certain belief, that those gone before who believed in him, have entered into that happier life . . .'. Everything about the cemetery cushions the reality of the finality of death and separation from all this world's treasures, including the families we love. The theme is supported by the air-conditioned alcoves to preserve the embalmed corpse, the organ music playing from speakers concealed in the shrubbery and the burial plots with their appealing names, 'Sunrise Slope', 'Slumberland', 'Haven of Peace'. It is a beautiful place and the Builder has successfully excluded almost all the depressing features of cemeteries the world over. By denuding death of its starkness, however, he has at the same time rendered the resurrection hope an insipid and paltry replica of life here on earth.

The prevailing trend of modern theology must also give account for the failure of modern man to recognize the seriousness of death by calling into question the traditional relationship between sin and death, so that a man

---

[1] An optional prayer in the new American Prayer Book begins, 'O God of grace and glory, we remember before you this day our brother (sister) N. We thank you for giving *him* to us. *his* family and friends, to know and to love as a companion on our earthly pilgrimage . . .' *The Book of Common Prayer* (Church Hymnal Corpora- tion, New York, 1979) p.493.

dies because he is a created being, not because he is a sinner. The New Testament, however, links death and sin. Sin causes men to approach death with fear; as the apostle Paul puts it, 'the sting of death is sin' (1 Cor. 15.56, cf. Rom. 5.12, 6.23). For the apostle death becomes a dreaded enemy, because it heralds the moment when we must stand before the judgment of God in the knowledge of our sinfulness. Reinhold Niebuhr comments on the Biblical view of the relation between sin and mortality:

> 'In this view mortality, insecurity and dependence are not of themselves evil but become the occasion of evil when man seeks in his pride to hide his mortality, to overcome his insecurity by his own power and to establish his independence. The ideal possibility would be that a man of perfect faith would not fear death because of his confidence that "neither death nor life . . . shall be able to separate us from the love of God, which is in Christ Jesus our Lord'. But since unbelief is the very basis of sin, it is impossible for sinful man to anticipate his end with equanimity'.[1]

When modern theology retreats from the seriousness of death it is not surprising that much modern liturgy follows suit. The Liturgical Commission, in its introduction to the report *Alternative Services Series 3 Funeral Services,* hoped 'that the remains of medieval gloom have finally given way to a more authentically Christian note of confidence and hope'.[2] Presumably they refer to the removal from their draft service of the burial anthem 'In the midst of life we are in death . . .' preceded by the quotation from Job 'Man that is born of a woman . . .' (Job 14.1, 2). Fortunately the approved service reinstated these, at least as an option.

An important point to make both in the service and the sermon is that one day another congregation will gather and the coffin at the front will be mine. Our death heralds our judgment.[3] The draft Series 3 service caught the right note when it included the prayer,

> 'Help us, Lord who are left here, to remember how short our time is. While we have the opportunity, lead us to repent of our sins, and to do what we have left undone.'[4]

(b) *The Hope of Resurrection.* The second and most obvious note for the preacher to strike at the funeral service is the hope of resurrection but it is by no means easy for the congregation to hear and receive the message. On one occasion a funeral cortege drew up at the covered porch of the crematorium. A beautiful wreath lay on the top of the casket. A football of white chrysanthemums rose out of a green field and blue and white irises added the finishing touch. The deceased, a supporter of Everton Football Club, died in the stand at the match. He had been a keen supporter of the club all his life and his family spoke with satisfaction of his death at the event which brought him the greatest pleasure in life. The funeral service went well. The minister took as his text Psalm 1 with its imagery

---

[1] Reinhold Niebuhr, *The Nature and Destiny of Man,* Vol. 1 (Nisbet: London, 1941) p.186.
[2] Report, The Liturgical Commission of the Church of England, *Alternative Services Series 3, Funeral Services,* GS 147, (SPCK, London, 1973), p.6.
[3] Hebrews 9.27. Many of the Roman Catholic lections for Burial Masses underline this point and I have included them in my list of funeral lessons below. See *Lectionary* (Geoffrey Chapman, London, 1969) pp.941-965.
[4] *op. cit.,* p.12. In the approved service the prayer is amended to read, 'Grant us, Lord, the wisdom and the grace to use aright the time that is left to us here on earth . . .'

reflected in the favourite crowd chorus of the time: 'Like a tree planted by the waterside, we shall not be moved'. There was only one disappointment. The family had written to the manager of the club to ask for his ashes to be scattered at the ground. The club, however, politely refused the request because they received too many similar enquiries. The family were upset because they had wanted their loved one to lie where, on a Saturday, he could catch the spirit and the thrill of the match.

This story illustrates poignantly, and reflects with some accuracy, a popular view of what happens at death. In spite of everything, things turn out alright and we survive, in some form, either to enjoy what death snatched away from us in this life or to experience a reversal of life's injustices, like Lazarus in the parable which Jesus told (Luke 16.19-31). Basic to this popular belief about life after death is the separation of soul and body and the immortality of the soul. Almost every *In Memoriam* column in the local paper provides evidence of this. 'Gentle Jesus up above, give our granny all our love'. Parents tell their children that granny has become an angel, even if that is hardly how they would have described her when she was alive! Our loved ones leave behind their bodies and go to a life where all is well, the inheritance of all sincere people who have kept the golden rule.

In 1974 the B.B.C. commissioned a poll by the Opinion Research Centre which may be compared with a similar Gallup Poll in 1963. Those who believed in life after death declined from 53% in 1963 to 39% in 1974. There was an almost exactly corresponding rise in the percentage of those who believed there was no life after death from 22% in 1963 to 35% in 1974. The real impact of this scepticism is of course hard to evaluate for, in the same period, believers in a 'spirit or life force' increased by 2% and the percentage of those who had no belief in God or a life force actually declined by 3% to just 6% of the sample.[1]

During October 1982, a survey was conducted among 3180 readers of *New Society*. Respondents were asked to say how much they believed in life after death. 21% believed 'quite a lot'. A further 40% believed 'some of the time'. 38% believed 'not at all'. In answering a further question, 27% believed in God 'quite a lot'. A further 33% believed 'some of the time'. 39% believed 'not at all'. Asked about their belief in Christianity, as many as 44% of responding readers said 'not at all',[2] but readers of *New Society* constitute a restricted category. A MORI poll in December 1989 showed that 74% of people in Britain said they believed in God, and more than two in three believe the essential elements of the nativity story.[3] In spite of a wide range of attitudes, in 1989, Britain still considered itself to be Christian. Put together, these figures give an indication of trends during the last two decades. Interest has increased in mysticism in general and Eastern religions in particular. This represents a revolt against the scientism of the sixties coupled with an uncertainty about the traditional alternatives of orthodox Christianity. Mysticism appeals because it is undogmatic by

1 *Sunday Telegraph* 13 October 1974.
2 *New Society*, Vol. 82, no. 1045 (25 November 1982) p.336.
3 *Sunday Times*, 24 December 1989.

nature and experiential in character. More particularly, the individual receives an everlasting significance which includes the idea of growth and development through many rebirths. At the same time the radical discontinuity between men and other creatures, such as Christianity has traditionally maintained, is removed. The unpopular concept of judgment is excluded whilst at the same time suffering and death are taken into the system with a realism and acceptance which Christianity has sometimes evaded. Finally the fascination with the occult and with the possibility of some kind of contact and solidarity with the unseen world of the dead has been compelling. In other words, a kaleidoscope of views reflects the pluralism of modern society. Undogmatic religious belief survives as strongly as ever and, at least at death and in the ceremonies which surround it, belief in survival continues with remarkable resilience.

The reader will have to look elsewhere for a serious engagement with these attitudes and for a fuller treatment of the theology of death.[1] But popular ideas stand in striking contrast to the Christian hope of resurrection which finds its roots in the Bible. The picture presented in the Bible is one of coherent development from doubt to assurance. In the Old Testament there is a profound scepticism about what happens at death. The heavens belong to the Lord and the earth is held in trust by the sons of men who live to bless the Lord, while the dead 'go down into silence' (Ps. 115.16-18). If there is survival at all, and we need to remember that in the Old Testament there is no separation of soul and body, then dead men's lips are silent. In some Old Testament writings, however, a clear belief in resurrection emerges (Is. 26.19, Ezek. 37.1-14). The resurrection is the revivifying of those who are now dead and buried. The event has a significance, not so much for the individual, as for the whole community of God's people who will live again and come home to their own land. But, although the dominant motif of resurrection refers to the whole community, one cannot escape the notion that at the resurrection, which is closely associated with God's judgment, a distinction will be made between individuals (Dan. 12.1-3). In spite of the obscurity of the text, Job expected to stand after death in an individual and special relation to God, as indeed he did during his life on earth (Job 19.25). The hope also of the psalmist was confident. 'As for me, I shall behold thy face in righteousness; when I awake, I shall be satisfied with beholding thy form' (Ps. 17.15).

The Pharisees formed the party in Jesus' day that set great store by the hope of the individual resurrection of the righteous and Jesus not only believed this but confirmed it in his own resurrection which is central to all Christian belief about death and the future (see Matt. 22.23-33). The resurrection of Jesus is the pledge of the Christian's resurrection to life with God and likeness to Jesus (1 Cor. 15.12-26). The Christian hopes for resurrection and not merely the survival of death or the saving of the immortal soul within a man. Even that passage in the New Testament which speaks of man as

---

1 See, e.g.: Eberhard Jüngel, *Death the Riddle and the Mystery* (St. Andrew's Press, Edinburgh, 1975); Helmut Thielicke, *Living with Death* (Eerdmans, Grand Rapids, U.S.A., 1983); Ray S. Sanderson, *Theology, Death and Dying* (Basil Blackwell, Oxford, 1986).

living in an earthly tent which is exchanged for 'a house not made with hands, eternal in the heavens' speaks not of the separation of soul and body but of the total transformation of the transient into the eternal (2 Cor. 5.1-4).

The problem arose for the early Christians when there was a lengthy delay in the coming of the Lord and the resurrection of the faithful. Paul suggested that they were asleep and therefore awaiting the resurrection (1 Thess. 4.13-18). Other New Testament passages imply the possibility of more conscious activity (Luke 16.19-31, 1 Pet. 3.19, 4.6). The ultimate hope, however, is resurrection. Christians have already experienced a spiritual resurrection through their identification with the death and resurrection of Christ symbolized in baptism (Rom. 6.3-16). The apostle John can say that we have already passed from death unto life (1 John 3.14). We hope in Christ to enter into the fullness of our inheritance with him at the day of Resurrection (Phil. 1.21-23). As John Donne put it:

'Death, be not proud, though some have called thee
Mighty and dreadful, thou art not so.
For those whom thou thinkest thou dost overthrow
Die not, poor Death, nor yet canst thou kill me . . .
One short sleep past, we wake eternally,
and death shall be no more. Death, thou shalt die.'[1]

The Funeral Service is therefore an Easter liturgy.[2] The resurrection of Jesus Christ lies at the heart of it and although he may have to cut right across the feelings and perceptions of the congregation which gathers, the preacher, who is true to his calling, proclaims the true Christian hope. The liturgy will support him in his task.

(c) *The Ultimate Unity of all Believers in Christ.* In the third place the preacher brings the hope of the ultimate unity of all God's people. Here again the preacher will cut across the anticipations of his people. The hope of most mourners centres upon the expectation that the deceased will rejoin his loved ones and one day we too will rejoin him. It is a perfectly natural response to the awful separation of death. It is not, however, what the Bible leads us to expect. In response to the Sadducees who were trying to trip him up on possible problems of polygamy at the resurrection, Jesus curtly replied, 'You are wrong, because you know neither the scriptures nor the power of God. For in the resurrection they neither marry nor are given in marriage, but are like angels in heaven' (Matt. 22.29, 30). The transformation is such that the question of reunion with those we love takes on a new dimension. We shall be changed. God will complete the process of change now taking place through the action of the Holy Spirit within us (2 Cor. 3.18). 'We shall not all sleep, but we shall be changed, in a moment, in the twinkling of an eye, at the last trumpet. For the trumpet

1 John Donne, *op. cit.* pp.283f.
2 The American *Book of Common Prayer* (1979) adds a note to the Burial Office; 'The liturgy for the dead is an Easter Liturgy. It finds all its meaning in the resurrection. Because Jesus was raised from the dead, we too shall be raised.' *op. cit.* p.507.

will sound, and the dead will be raised imperishable, and we shall be changed' (1 Cor. 15.51, 52). The Christian hopes that he will become like Jesus (1 John 3.2). Christians in that day will pre-occupy themselves in Jesus Christ and, in him, we will be united with all who love and serve him. In our congregation we had a widower who had recently lost his wife. He came each Sunday to the Holy Communion because, in that service, he discovered a continuing link with the one he still loved. He explained that it was something which they could still share and they would go on sharing in Christ to eternity.

Not all those who mourn can receive this as good news. They have bound up their lives in the one they have lost and the only hope, as they see it, is a joyful reunion in a life similar to the one they have known on earth. This makes the task of the pastoral preacher all the harder when he comes to speak at the funeral. Commenting on the separation by death of two married people who dearly loved each other, Martin Luther once described God as 'the greatest adulterer' because he broke the closest human relationship.[1] Any future reunion will transcend exclusive relationships on earth and will bring us all together in the worship and praise of God (see 1 Cor. 15.28, Eph. 1.10, Col. 1.20). The prayer in the ASB 1980 Funeral Service puts it well: 'May God in his infinite love and mercy bring the whole Church, living and departed in the Lord Jesus, to a joyful resurrection and the fulfilment of his eternal kingdom.' The Archbishops' Commission on Christian Doctrine thrashed out this prayer for the dead in 1971. In commenting upon it the Report states,

> '. . . we believe that ultimate and complete bliss is not available for any until it is available for all. The formula states that the unity of living and departed is only to be found "in the Lord Jesus". It mentions the "joyful resurrection" because this unambiguously refers to a future consummation and not to any hypothetical intermediate state.'[2]

What can the preacher say about the hoped-for reunion with those we love? We may say that we shall be united in Christ (2 Cor. 4.14). We may say that those who die in Christ are happy, for 'blessed are the dead who die in the Lord henceforth' (Rev. 14.13). One further hopeful text assures us that 'we are surrounded by so great a cloud of witnesses' (Heb. 12.1). If these include Christians who have finished their course and are now watching over us, then we may assume that one day we will join them and share with them a continuing concern for God's work in the world. The unity which we now enjoy with other believers through the Holy Spirit will attain its own goal as the whole Church draws together in Christ.

---

[1] ed. Theodore G. Tappert, Luther: *Letters of Spiritual Counsel* (The Library of Christian Classics, Vol. XVIII, SCM, London, 1955) p.73. 'Unser Herre Gott ist der groste Ehebrecher'.

[2] *Prayer and the Departed,* A Report of the Archbishops' Commission on Christian Doctrine (SPCK, London, 1971) p.51.

2. THE PREACHER'S NEEDS

Apart from the obvious need for the preacher to have a Biblical approach to death and resurrection, he has two needs relating to his own self-awareness and sensitivity. He has to come to terms with his own death and he must empathize with the bereaved to whom he speaks. All preaching, and particularly preaching at death, reveals the inmost being of the preacher. Sermons, like buildings, tell us much about the people who design them. When chiselled in the study through a close study of the scriptures, they may unwittingly reveal a detachment from the congregation, a difficulty in handling relationships in times of crisis and even an unwillingness on the part of the preacher to face the personal challenge presented by the tragedy of another. Equally, if sermons merely echo the feelings of the congregation, reinforce and reiterate platitudes, the preacher reveals his own lack of security in the faith and his inability to rest in the promises of God. It is always tempting at the moment of crisis to fall into one of these two errors. Therefore the preacher at funerals needs to gain the freedom and the integrity to bring a message which is true to God's Word and to himself, offered eyeball to eyeball to his congregation in their need.

(i) The minister must come to terms with his own death

This is less easy than it sounds in a day when death is a taboo subject of conversation in spite of the increasing volume of literature about it. Nor is it easy for the minister who has at his disposal the best means of all, religious belief, for avoiding the impact of death. Robert E. Neale has listed some of the peculiar temptations of ministers:

> 'He reassures the dying patient and the bereaved survivors with all the tools at his disposal. As soon as he suspects that people are going to open themselves to him with all their suffering, he cuts them off with "The Lord is my shepherd" or "Let us pray". Scripture and prayers are used by the anxious minister to shut people up and shut them out of his presence. Such reassurance for the patient is premature and its basic purpose is to reassure the minister himself. He may spend much time with the dying and the bereaved; he is a very busy man, always around, always doing something helpful. This may look good, but the busyness is frequently a way of avoiding the problems surrounding death . . . At the one time when death is most obvious to a Christian community, the Church flees into dogmas of eternal life. That little item in between life and eternity gets lost'.[1]

In making a similar point, Elisabeth Kubler-Ross recounts how one theology student learnt his lesson, literally through confronting the possibility of his own death through cancer. The successive experiences of shock, dismay, disbelief, anger, hope and fear ensured that he would never use empty words to either the terminally ill or the recently bereaved.[2]

Many ministers obviously find it impossible to face so squarely the prospect of imminent death. We may, however, try to take our own death into our understanding of Christian faith and life. It may not be necessary, like John Donne, to put an open coffin in the bedroom but it is good to face it with the same realism. The author was much helped some years ago as he ministered to a very independent lady who discovered she was dying from a form of

1 Robert E. Neale, *The Art of Dying* (Harper and Row, New York, 1973) pp.12f.
2 Elisabeth Kubler-Ross, *On Death and Dying* (Tavistock Press, London, 1970) p.227.

creeping paralysis. She had been a strong-willed and independent member of the church, one of God's awkward squad, and in her home the pillar upon whom all the family relied. Slowly but surely all her faculties left her. She proceeded from crutches to wheel-chair to being a bed-patient incapable even of feeding herself. Now she depended on the family as much as they once had depended upon her. But, as so many ministers will testify from their pastoral experience, this apparent tragedy turned into a quite remarkable spiritual pilgrimage. Her faith, which had seemed to rest so much in her own powers and resources, now resided in the Christ who was still with her when she could do nothing for him. She 'died' before she died, and she rose before the resurrection in which she will be raised with Christ. A death and resurrection took place before our very eyes, and it was possible at least in part to learn the lesson with her. In a similar way the apostle Paul related to the death and resurrection of Jesus Christ to the point where he was confident that nothing in life or death could separate him from the love of God in Christ Jesus. (Rom. 8.37-39).

We are speaking here of the heart of the Christian faith symbolized in our baptism. The difficulty is that the death and resurrection of our baptism need daily renewal. That is the hardest spiritual challenge of them all. Certainly many Christians have known such an experience in the past where nothing was more important than to live and die for Christ. But few of us dare say with Paul, 'I die every day!' (1 Cor. 15.31) or 'I have been crucified with Christ; it is no longer I who live, but Christ who lives in me; and the life I now live in the flesh I live by faith in the Son of God who loved me and gave himself for me' (Gal.2.20). Yet here is the secret of a proper Christian autonomy in the face of death, an autonomy which will resist both the temptation to take refuge in dogmatic assertion and also the temptation to surrender to sentiment or to unhelpful sympathy. Hanns Lilje, the German church leader once condemned to death under the Nazis, tells how in prison he added a quarter of an hour of daily meditation on death to his regular rule of life. He describes it as a holy conflict with death and concludes:

> 'Such experiences open up a new dimension of depth in human existence. No one knows the nature of man completely who has not seen him when he is completely helpless, for then he shows himself as he really is; whatever remains when he has reached this extreme limit of human life it becomes clear why God is with those who are despised, outcast, tortured, imprisoned, disinherited and solitary'.[1]

(ii) The preacher must empathize with the bereaved

Empathy is to be distinguished from sympathy. To offer sympathy is to enter into, and to share, the feelings and views of the other person. To empathize is to have an accurate awareness and understanding of the feelings, emotions and behaviour of the other person. Clergymen could learn a lesson here from the undertaker, whom they frequently meet in the course of a bereavement visit and to whom they frequently give a bad press. He has a helpful but not unrespectful detachment as he goes about the practical arrangements for the funeral. He tries to be aware of what the

---

[1] Hanns Lilje, *Interlude in a Nazi Prison* (Decision Magazine, London, May 1965) p.9. extracted from Hanns Lilje, *The Valley of the Shadow* (Muhlenberg Press, Philadelphia)).

bereaved really want and does not normally try to impose upon them inappropriate suggestions. At this point his cool professionalism helps the family, together with his attempt to be unobtrusive in playing his own part.

In visiting the bereaved Colin Murray Parkes argues that the clergyman should approach like any other friendly person;

'He too should be prepared to show by his manner acceptance of grief and particularly acceptance of the bitter anger against God and man that is likely to be expressed. He will not help matters by returning the anger, by meeting emotion with dogma or agony with glib assurance. He will help best by listening, and if invited to do so, by trying to collaborate with the bereaved person in an honest attempt to "get things straight". The clergyman who is "in tune" with his parishioner may be able to find the right prayer or a helpful biblical quotation, but it is tempting to hide behind such "easy" answers and avoid involvement by too readily prescribing "magical" solutions to grief'.[1]

With so many calls upon his time and his ears, the clergyman finds it hard to listen carefully before he preaches at the funeral. Sometimes, at a crematorium service for someone long since moved from the area for instance, it will be impossible. He may, however, understand what death does to us all.

(a) Death calls into question everything which we consider worthwhile in life. Just as, when we fall in love, the world seems bright, new and translucent, so when death comes to one we love a shadow falls upon everything. The things we have treasured lose their value. Relationships change. We remember how, on Good Friday, the friends and relatives of Jesus clung together but the relationship took on a new dimension. The one who bound them closely together left them and they had to build new bridges and to try them out. Sometimes when the relative has been demanding, awkward and cantankerous the effect of his death is no less disturbing for those who have loved him painfully. When David heard of the death of his troublesome and rebellious son Absalom he was deeply moved and wept in grief which was deep and heartfelt (2 Sam. 18.31-19.8). Interestingly it was a sorrow with which the ordinary people tried to sympathize and which Joab rejected as a sign of weakness and disloyalty to his friends. One cannot help feeling that had Samuel been around he might have offered the king the empathetic ear which he needed at his moment of bereavement when, paradoxically, the relief which people felt he ought to experience was overtaken by the broken heart of a bereaved father.

(b) Bereavement also challenges the faith which we have in God. 'Why did God allow this to happen?' A number of surveys have shown that the tendency of the bereaved to blame themselves, others or God is a common feature.[2] We find at least one example in the scriptures where the world of two sisters, Martha and Mary, is in danger of caving in with the death of their beloved brother Lazarus (John 11.1-44). Their hopes, pinned upon the presence of Jesus, collapsed because he arrived in Bethany too late. 'Lord, if you had been here, my brother would not have died'. Is there a note

[1] Colin Murray Parkes, *Bereavement* (Tavistock Press, London, 1972) p.170.
[2] Parkes *op. cit.* p.211.

15

of rebuke in Martha's voice? At least she is unwilling to accept his death. For all her faith in the resurrection at the last day, she attempts to find some object of blame or hope. Orthodox dogma is no solution to her tears and despair; not even the life-giving words of Jesus, which Martha says she believes, can stem the flow. Until Lazarus was raised, according to the apostle, the ministry of Jesus was singularly ineffective in allaying the grief of the two sisters. But at least he was there. He was able to take in the situation, 'he was deeply moved in spirit and troubled'.

(c) Preoccupation with the deceased, as though he were still alive, is another common reaction to bereavement. Obviously spiritualist religion thrives on the hope that it is possible to remain in contact with the departed. The resurrection of Christ does not, however, encourage such speculation. Jesus forbade Mary Magdalene to hold on to his risen body but rather instructed her to go and tell the brethren of his impending departure to be with his heavenly father (John 20.17). The disciples' attachment to their risen Lord is significantly different from the sometimes dangerous pre-occupation of the bereaved with the deceased. For the disciples it led to a commitment to the fulfilment of Jesus' own mission to the world. They loved and worshipped Christ but in such a way that they did not close themselves to the rest of the world but rather opened themselves to it. If we can help the bereaved to the point where the sense of their dear one's presence spurs them to share his concern and service it will help in the healing process.

Altogether Colin Murray Parkes lists seven common reactions to bereave-ment and they are worth quoting in full:

1. A process of realization, i.e. the way in which the bereaved person moves from denial or avoidance of recognition of the loss towards acceptance.
2. An alarm reaction—anxiety, restlessness, and the physiological accompaniments of fear.
3. An urge to search for and to find the lost person in some form.
4. Anger and guilt, including outbursts against those who press the bereaved person towards premature acceptance of his loss.
5. Feelings of internal loss of self or mutilation.
6. Identification phenomena—the adoption of traits, mannerisms, or symptoms of the lost person, with or without a sense of his presence within the self.
7. Pathological variants of grief, i.e. the reaction may be excessive and prolonged or inhibited and inclined to emerge in distorted form.[1]

The minister, who is to preach at the funeral, will need to emphathize with reactions like these. If it has not been a first-hand experience, the minister will need to listen with great care to the story of the one who has been through it.[2]

[1] Parkes *op. cit.* p.183.
[2] e.g. Liz McNeill Taylor, *Living with Loss – 'A Book for the Widowed'* (Fontana, Collins, Glasgow, 1983).

Some years ago a powerful television documentary told the story of the decline and eventual death of a nineteen-year-old drug addict. The programme, *Gale is Dead,* included interviews and background material ending with a film of the funeral service conducted by an Anglican clergyman. The minister read the service with care and at the end shook hands with the mourners. The mourners complained afterwards, however, that the minister obviously knew nothing about Gale. Whether or not he could help it, it is certainly true that the minister did not engage with the friends of Gale who had tried to help her through nineteen years of rejection and isolation. There was a lack of empathy for the congregation.

A trial sermon for the supposed funeral of a known petty criminal displayed a different lack of empathy. In the endeavour to say something comforting to the mourners, the student managed to convey to the congregation the impression that he was good at heart, unselfish, and all would be well in the end. The preacher was in collusion with the deceased and, in spite of his attempt to be careful in his affirmations about the departed, he left his hearers with the impression of a man who had become a saint in his death. It would not have been surprising if the congregation had gone away with disdain for the church. The detachment of the one minister and the sympathy of the other, in the examples quoted, highlight the need to be accurately aware of the feelings and needs of those to whom we preach at death.

3. THE RESOURCES OF THE PREACHER

The preacher needs, if he is to preach effectively, to know as much as possible about the family and the congregation which gathers for the funeral. He also needs to be secure in his own hope of resurrection through Christ. If he is not, both the preacher and the congregation will sense a lack of credibility which renders the sermon either platitudinous or vacuous in its affirmations. Apart from that personal preparation of himself, the preacher has to be able to bring to bear the revealed promises of God from the Bible. In the pages which follow I try simply to list those passages from the scriptures which best suit the themes of life's brevity, resurrection hope and the reunion in Christ. Funeral liturgies have used most of these passages as lessons for many centuries.[1] I also list some suitable psalms which capture the heartache of man in his moments of greatest need and a selection of Christian hymns as suitable replacements for 'The Lord's my Shepherd' and 'Abide with Me'. Finally, I include four brief sermon outlines which try to tackle scripture exposition in the context of four difficult pastoral situations; a suicide, the death of a child, the funeral of a public figure and the crematorium service for a stranger. These sermons are only sample outlines prepared for this booklet and need to be filled out and developed in relation to the pastoral context. I have not included a sermon for the funeral of a known and active Christian. Such sermons, in my experience, are a joy to prepare and deliver.

FUNERAL LESSONS

Deuteronomy	33.1, 26-29	(underneath are the everlasting arms)
Job	19.21-27a	(I know that my redeemer lives)
Isaiah	25.6-9	(He will swallow up death for ever)
	40.1-11	(the glory of the Lord shall be revealed)
	61.1-3	(the oil of gladness instead of mourning)
Lamentations	3.17-26	(the steadfast love of the Lord never ceases)
	3.31-38	(though he cause grief, he will have compassion)
Ezekiel	36.25-28	(you shall be my people, and I will be your God)
Daniel	12.1-3	(many of those who sleep shall awake)
Wisdom	3.1-9	(the souls of the righteous are in the hand of God)
	4.7-11, 13-15	(his soul was pleasing unto the Lord)
Matthew	5.1-12	(rejoice and be glad, for great is your reward in heaven)
	11.25-30	(come to me, all who labour)
	25.1-13	(you know neither the day nor the hour)
	25.31-46	(inherit the kingdom prepared for you)
Mark	5.22-24,35-43	(the child is not dead but sleeping)
	10.13-16	(let the children come to me)
	15.33-39, 16.1-6	(He has risen, he is not here)
Luke	7.11-17	(young man, I say to you, arise)
	12.35-40	(you also must be ready)
	23.33, 39-43	(today you will be with me in Paradise)
	24.13-35	(Jesus himself drew near and went with them)

[1] See Geoffrey Rowell, *The Liturgy of Burial* (Alcuin Club/SPCK, London, 1977) p.131f.

John	5.19-25	(the Father raises the dead and gives them life)
	6.35-40	(I will raise him up at the last day)
	6.51-58	(he who eats this bread will live for ever)
	10.11-16, 27-29	(I am the good shepherd)
	11 17-27	(I am the resurrection and the life)
	12.23-28	(unless a grain of wheat falls into the earth)
	14.1-6	(in my Father's house are many rooms)
	17.24-26	(I desire that they . . . may be with me)
Acts	10.34-43	(he is the one ordained by God to be judge)
	20.17-38	(if only I may accomplish my course)
Romans	5.1-11	(reconciled to God by the death of his son)
	5.15-22	(those who receive the abundance of grace . . . reign in life)
	6.3-12	(united with him in a resurrection like his)
	8.14-25	(the glorious liberty of the children of God)
	8.31-39	(who shall separate us from the love of Christ)
	14.7-9	(Lord of both the dead and the living)
1 Corinthians	13.4-13	(then I shall understand fully)
	15.20-26	(in Christ shall all be made alive)
	15.35-43	(how are the dead raised ?)
	15.51-58	(victory through our Lord Jesus Christ)
2 Corinthians	1.2-5	(Father of mercies and God of all comfort)
	4.7-18	(things that are unseen are eternal)
	5.1-9	(at home with the Lord)
Ephesians	3.14-21	(the love of Christ which surpasses knowledge)
Philippians	3.8-21	(our citizenship is in heaven)
1 Thessalonians	4.13-18	(we shall always be with the Lord)
	5.1-11	(whether we wake or sleep we might live with him)
2 Timothy	2.8-13	(we shall also live with him)
Hebrews	10.19-25	(confidence to enter the sanctuary)
1 Peter	1.3-9	(a living hope through the resurrection)
1 John	3.1-3	(we shall see him as he is)
Revelation	7.9-17	(God will wipe away every tear)
	21.1-7	(I make all things new)

PSALMS FOR FUNERALS

4   (in peace I will both lie down and sleep)
5   (make thy way straight before me)
15   (who shall dwell on thy holy hill ?)
16   (in thy presence there is fullness of joy)
20   (the Lord answer you in the day of trouble)
23   (the Lord is my shepherd)
24   (he will receive blessing from the Lord)
26   (thy steadfast love is before my eyes)
27   (the Lord is my light and my salvation)
30   (joy comes with the morning)
39   (Lord, let me know my end)
41   (in thy presence for ever)
42   (my soul thirsts for God)
43   (send out thy light and thy truth)
46   (God is our refuge and strength)
56   (put thou my tears in thy bottle)
61   (lead thou me to the rock that is higher than I)

63 (thy steadfast love is better than life)
71 (thou art my rock and my fortress)
84 (how lovely is thy dwelling place)
90 (Lord, thou hast been our dwelling place)
91 (he who dwells in the shelter of the Most High)
103 (as a father pities his children)
106 (remember me, O Lord, when thou showest favour to thy people)
116 (thou hast delivered my soul from death)
118 (open to me the gates of righteousness)
121 (the Lord will keep your going out and your coming in)
130 (out of the depths I cry to thee)
139 (whither shall I go from thy spirit)
142 (my portion in the land of the living)
143 (enter not into judgment with thy servant)
146 (the Lord lifts up those who are bowed down)

HYMNS FOR FUNERALS[1]

A safe stronghold our God is still
Abide with me
As pants the hart
Behold the amazing gift of love
Blest be the everlasting God
Children of the heavenly king
'Come unto me, ye weary'
Crown Him with many crowns
Dear Lord and Father of mankind
Father, hear the prayer we offer
For ever with the Lord
Hallelujah! Hallelujah! Hearts to Heaven
How bright these glorious spirits shine!
How firm a foundation
How sweet the name of Jesus
I cannot tell why He, whom angels worship
I heard the voice of Jesus say
I know that my Redeemer lives
Immortal love, for ever full
In heavenly love abiding
Jesus lives! thy terrors now
Jesu, Lover of my soul
Jesus! the name high over all
Lead kindly light
Lead us, heavenly Father, lead us
Lord of our life, and God of our salvation

Love's redeeming work is done
My hope is built on nothing less
Now thank we all our God
O God of Bethel! by whose hand
O God, our help in ages past
O Love that wilt not let me go
O the deep, deep love of Jesus!
Peace, perfect peace, in this dark world of sin?
Rejoice, the Lord is King!
Rock of ages, cleft for me
Seek ye first, not earthly pleasure
Sun of my soul, Thou Saviour dear
Teach me Thy way, O Lord
Ten thousand times ten thousand
The day Thou gavest, Lord, is ended
The King of love my Shepherd is
The Lord's my Shepherd, I'll not want
The strife is o'er, the battle done
Thine be the glory
Thine for ever! God of love
Thou art the Way; by Thee alone
Through all the changing scenes of life
'We rest on Thee,' our shield and our defender

1 See also Alan Dunstan, *These are the Hymns* (SPCK, London, 1973) pp.55-58.

SERMON 1: THE PAIN OF LOVE

Aim; That love may conquer the doubts and fears of my congregation in the face of tragedy.

Context; A suicide or a bitter tragedy has struck a family in the parish.

Text; 1 Corinthians 13.12. '. . . then I shall understand fully, even as I have been fully understood.'

Few moments in our lives leave us more helpless than moments of personal tragedy. To whom may we protest our incapacity to understand? Like Job we may shout to God that man is a weak and fragile creature. And God will listen. But he will not answer our challenge to explain it all. As long as we live on earth our knowledge is imperfect and we shall see in a mirror dimly.

The Christian hope, however, does not leave us for ever in despair. The day will come when we shall understand fully and see for ourselves face to face. The riddles will be resolved. In the meantime we can take heart that, despite our partial knowledge of God, he knows and understands us fully.

We know God understands because Jesus understands. 'For we have not a high priest who is unable to sympathize with our weaknesses, but one who in every respect has been tempted as we are, yet without sinning' (Hebrews 4.15). He knows what it is to be weary, disappointed, deserted and even what it is to feel abandoned by God himself. Yet in none of these experiences did the pain separate him from his father in heaven and, through it all, his father loved him. God loves us too even in our experience of rejection, much in the same way as an earthly father loves his children through their feeling of being unloved and uncared for. One day they will discover, and we will discover, that our heavenly Father's love does not ebb and flow like the tide but guards us constantly whether or not we perceive it.

Even today, however, in the midst of all the confusion of heart and mind, 'Love never ends'. There is no end to the love of God in Christ, 'Love bears all things, believes all things, hopes all things, endures all things'. Not even death itself can separate us from the love of God.

When that love of God is shed abroad in our hearts we, like Jesus, conquer the power of death. In the temptation to lose faith, we will trust the one who loved us to the end. In the temptation to give way to despair, we will hope in the one who rose from the grave. In the love of Christ we will not find the answer to all our questions but we will be carried, as on a wave, through the turmoil of our doubts and fears to land safely on the shore of ultimate understanding.

SERMON 2: ASLEEP IN CHRIST

Aim;   that my congregation may lose their fear in the faith that this child is asleep in Christ.

Context;   The funeral of a child.

Text;   Mark 5.36. 'Do not fear, only believe'.

The family, the friends and the whole community feel deeply the death of a child. So much was hoped for and apparently so little was achieved. Few things in life leave us more helpless, hopeless and faithless than the death of a child.

While she was alive our hope was alive. Like Jairus perhaps we even expected a miracle from Jesus, 'Come and lay your hands on her so that she may be well and live'. But now she is dead and we are tempted to think that there is no longer any need or use in troubling Jesus.

But Jesus does not give up easily in the face of the grief of the family and friends. 'The child is not dead but sleeping'. At first such a response may seem to be a cruel joke at the expense of the mourners; they judge that it is and laugh him to scorn. And there may well be those in church who are here more out of respect for the family than out of any sympathy for the message of resurrection enshrined in the service.

To the family, however, and to the friends of Jesus there is, even in the midst of this tragedy, a note of hope. Jesus says to the father of the child, 'Do not fear, only believe'. For those who will look to Jesus as the hope of the world death is a sleep from which the dead in Christ will one day awake. He is the longed-for Messiah who raises the dead. In this confidence deep-seated fear gives way to peace, gnawing doubt to faith and dreadful despair to hope.

Unlike the daughter of Jairus this little child will not live again on the earth as we know it and our sorrow is natural. St. Chrysostom one said, 'Weep at the death of a dear one as if you are bidding farewell to one setting out on a journey'.[1] But the journey has an ending. There will be an awakening. The promise of Jesus assures us of it.

'Let the children come to me, do not hinder them; for to such belongs the kingdom of God' (Mark 10.14). They are close to his heart as the sheep of his flock. 'My sheep hear my voice, and I know them, and they follow me; and I give them eternal life, and they shall never perish, and no one shall snatch them out of my hand'. (John 10.27, 28).

This child is asleep in Christ—until that day when Jesus comes as he did to the home of Jairus and says, 'Little girl, I say to you, arise.'

[1] Homily on John xii (on John xi.1-29); lxxv. quoted by Rowell *op. cit.* p.22.

SERMON 3: CREATION WAITS . . .

Aim;   that my congregation may hold to the ultimate hope for the world through Christ.

Context;   The funeral of a public figure.

Text;   Romans 8.19, 21. 'For the creation waits with eager longing for the revealing of the sons of God . . . because the creation itself will be set free from its bondage to decay and obtain the glorious liberty of the children of God.'

When a public figure dies we are particularly conscious of the fact that he cannot be replaced. The world is poorer for this loss. He had much to give and he was a kind of symbol of the life of this community. Each one of us in some way identifies with his work.

Of course his work still lives on. His example and his commitment continue with us, hopefully to challenge us to the same kind of unstinting service. But there is an ultimate dimension to every man's work and that is underlined by the Christian hope of resurrection.

Sadly, we sometimes limit our perspective beyond the grave to a hope of personal survival. It is natural enough to seek an eternal significance for the individual, but the hope of resurrection is bigger than that. Paul says that the whole of creation is looking forward to the day.

'Creation itself will be set free . . .' In this life we are conscious of the limitations of all our efforts to create a better world. We are often frustrated and are tempted to wonder whether it is worthwhile to carry on. The answer is that it most certainly is. We are working towards the goal which one day God himself will achieve.

God will bring about all that in our better moments we hope for. There will be an end to injustice, oppression and inequality. And this hope has been sealed for us in the resurrection of Jesus Christ from the dead. The first Easter Day ushered in the new age of hope and confidence in the face of the sorrows of the world. With zeal and dedication the disciples of Jesus Christ set out upon the Master's own task of bringing reconciliation to men and nations. They are not preserved, any more than he was, from suffering but they have the knowledge that in the end his kingdom will come. And they have the assurance that all that they do on earth is a kind of announcement and advertisement of that which is to come.

In the light of this hope we remember with thanksgiving the contribution of men and women who give so much to our community. 'None of us lives to himself, and none of us dies to himself' (Romans 14.7). We are caught up in the life of each other and, even more, we are caught up in the eternal purpose of God. And that is why the Christian hopes in Christ. In him we have the perfect model and, by faith in him, we defy even death itself in the confidence that in the Lord our labour is not in vain.

SERMON 4: IN THE MIDST OF DEATH . . .

Aim;   that my congregation may hold to Jesus as the source of hope through death and judgment.

Context;   The funeral of a stranger at the crematorium.

Text;   John 11.25. 'I am the resurrection and the life; he who believes in me, though he die, yet shall he live . . .'

'Do you believe this?' The question comes to you and me as well as to Martha at a time like this. When we have lost someone we love dearly it is hard to say what we believe. While there is life there is hope, but doubt stalks with death.

'Lord, if you had been here, my brother would not have died.' There is disappointment. Martha and Mary had sent for Jesus in the confidence that he would meet their need, but he had not come in time. There is often disappointment at death. If only Jesus had come! He would have brought healing and hope and something worth living for. We are all tempted to say the same, 'if only . . .'

A rebuke is implied. The sisters may have suspected, or possibly they knew, that Jesus had delayed his coming. There is a natural tendency to attribute blame at the time of death. We blame God or other people or even ourselves. Sometimes there even arises within us an anger which takes us by surprise.

But here comes Jesus with his strange word of comfort, 'your brother will rise again'. This is not what the sisters want at all. They want their brother back now. It is small consolation to them to know that he will be raised at the last day. Are not these the suspect words of the religious teacher? They know what they ought to believe. Martha will even confess that Jesus is the Christ but her heart breaks and she believes only with her head. Nevertheless, when everything within you cries against it, believe it; Jesus is the resurrection and the life.

Now they have come to the grave surrounded by compassionate friends. Jesus is there 'deeply moved in spirit and troubled.' How can he show them that what they reckon disaster is a gateway to life with God? How can they come to see that he, Jesus, is the ground of faith and hope? He will raise the dead.

'Many . . . believed in him.' Lazarus was raised to live a few more years on earth but what really counted was that for these believers Jesus drew the sting of death. If Jesus raises the dead, and if he himself is raised, then there is hope eternal for the sad and sorrowing. But it is a hope we must claim for ourselves in the face of our own death and judgment. We shall not overcome the finality of the grave by an optimism which avoids that certainty. Lazarus will die again and we will die. If Christ will bring us to the resurrection of the dead, it will be via God's judgment before which we dare to stand only by faith in Christ.

24